A Bible Song Living Journal

† THE BOOKS OF MOSES

Volume 1

Written and Illustrated by
Rich Melheim

FAITH
INKUBATORS

THE BOOKS OF MOSES

Bible Song Living Journal - Volume I

Copyright © 2006 Faith Inkubators, 423 South Main St.
Stillwater, MN, 55082 Toll Free Phone: 1-888-55FAITH
In Minnesota (651) 430-0762, Fax (651) 430-2377

Written and Illustrated by Rich Melheim
Original Paintings by Dr. He Qi
(www.heqiarts.com)
Verbatim Bible Songs for all verses by
Faith Inkubators Music Guild
Signing for all verses by Christy Smith
(www.christyskids.tv)
Design elements by Lookout Design
(www.lookoutdesign.com)
Production Direction by
Jedi Master Ben Dolmar

Online music for each Bible verse, sign language, PowerPoint®
presentations, art projects, worship aids, lyric sheets, piano scores and
a myriad of additional resources are included in a membership to the Bible
Song Sunday school system. Our Bible Song curriculum is designed for
Sunday school, rotational classes, intergenerational learning, parochial schools,
home-schooling and weekday children's arts.
Learn more about the system and membership at www.faithink.com

CIP

ISBN 0-9785621-2-7

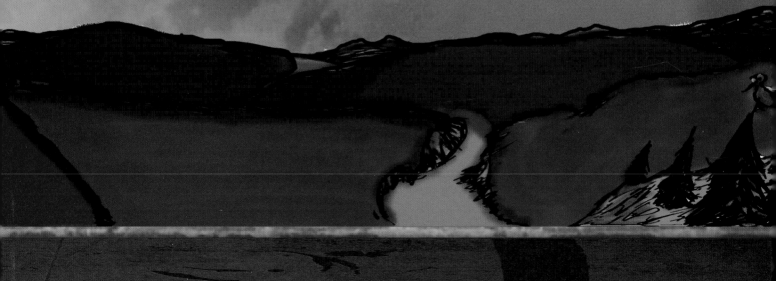

Praising God with Arts & Hands and Voices™

Sing, sign and art your way from one end of the Bible to the other with this fun new way to learn your favorite Scriptures by arts and by hearts. This **Living Journal** is designed to take you and your family into the Books of Moses from Creation to the edge of the Promised Land. Learn key Bible stories in cartoons. Find the **hidden verse** in each story. Then hop **online** to listen to the verse in song (verbatim) and learn it in sign language at **www.faithink.com.**

Take a few minutes tonight and every night to share the **FINK Five**—Highs & Lows, a verse, talk, prayer, and blessing—with your family. If you do this, you hold in your hands a tool that will help you learn about our awesome God **and** keep your family close all through your growing years.

the Bible Song Living Journals

FAITH INKUBATORS

THE NIGHTLY JOURNAL

Care to have some fun, keep your family communicating every night, and grow in your understanding of yourself and God? This **Bible Song Living Journal** is set up to do just that. Think of it as a conversation starter combined with a **family faith diary**. Simply get together with your family members for five minutes every night and follow the order outlined below. Record a sentence or two about your highs, lows, and prayers in the spaces provided. Use this tool regularly and you will certainly grow **closer** as a **family**. You will also be able to look back on your entire childhood faith journey one day and see where you have been, who you have become, and where God has taken you.

THE FINK FIVE STEPS (HOME HUDDLE)

The most important part of all this happens at home in a simple five-step process which the good folks at Faith Inkubators like to call the **FINK Five Steps** (or the "Home Huddle"). Here's how it works: Whoever is going to bed first in your house calls **"Huddle Up!"** Everyone must drop what they're doing, turn off the television and computer, put down their homework, and gather in a room of the convener's choice. Then take turns going through these five simple steps:

Try these hand motions to help you remember

THE FINK FIVE STEPS

1. Thumbs up/thumbs down (Highs & Lows); 2. Point to the Sky (Read the Assigned Bible Verse); 3. Cross your fingers (T for Talk); 4. Thumb to Ring (Prayer has a promise, too!); 5. Little Finger Up (Sometimes the biggest blessings come from the smallest places).

1. **SHARE** HIGHS & LOWS OF THE DAY

2. **READ** SING AND SIGN THE VERSE OF THE WEEK USING YOUR BIBLES

3. **TALK** ABOUT HOW THIS WEEK'S KEY VERSE RELATES TO YOUR HIGHS & LOWS

4. **PRAY** FOR YOUR HIGHS & LOWS, FOR YOUR FAMILY, AND FOR THE WORLD

5. **BLESS** ONE ANOTHER USING THE WEEKLY BLESSING PROVIDED

THE FINK FIVE

FIVE STEPS TO KEEPING YOUR FAMILY TOGETHER IN A WORLD THAT CAN TEAR YOU APART

New FINKlinks Online

There are a pile of surprises and fun new theme-related resources awaiting you online each night to enrich your Home Huddle experience. Play the **Name That Verse** game live with family and friends. Listen to and learn the week's key Bible verse in **song** and **American Sign Language**. Purchase the tune if you wish to carry it along or play it in the car this week. You can also view and purchase signed and numbered **artist proofs** of the cartoons by Rich Melheim, plus beautiful supplemental art on each theme by China's most amazing contemporary Christian artist, Dr. He Qi (www.heqiarts.com). Simply head on over to **www.faithink.com** and enter the FINKlink code listed for each specific theme.

At Church or School

For churches, home-schoolers and parochial schools using the Bible Song curriculum, each theme in this book also comes with **PowerPoint®** presentations, art projects, Reader's Theaters, and a treasure trove of **additional resources** designed to connect what you're learning at church and school with your nightly family conversations. In the curriculum, each theme is unveiled in art, songs, cartoons, Reader's Theater skits, and learning games. Small groups then enter a creative arts time called **Art Attack** to prepare arts to show off in a "show and tell" and in **congregational worship**.

At the Beginning of the Year

Use the next two pages to personalize this yearbook. Ask your parents to help you **record** the information requested. Then prepare to **share it** with your friends at church or school as a way to get to know one another. Then hop to the last page of this book and play **Operation Spyglass** to get to know this journal. Add photos of your friends and family in the spaces provided as a snap-shot of who you are at this moment in time.

At the **end of the year,** add some photos and use the final pages to summarize where you've been. You may look back on this book one day and see just how much fun it was to go through the Bible with such an **awesome family, awesome friends,** and your **awesome God!**

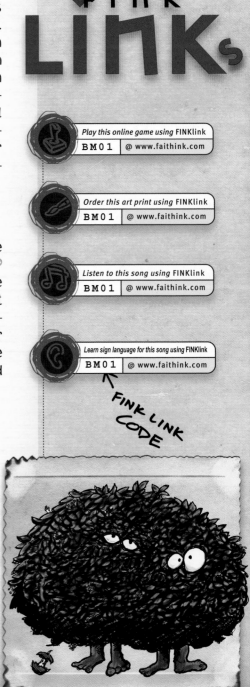

FINK
LINKs

Play this online game using FINKlink
BM01 | @ www.faithink.com

Order this art print using FINKlink
BM01 | @ www.faithink.com

Listen to this song using FINKlink
BM01 | @ www.faithink.com

Learn sign language for this song using FINKlink
BM01 | @ www.faithink.com

FINK LINK CODE

THIS BOOK BELONGS TO:

Take a moment to personalize this Living Journal. Include information about yourself, your family and your friends at church or school. Look back, look to the moment and look ahead to where you're going!

Name

Age & Grade   Today's Date

Phone   Email/IM

Birth date   Baptism Day

My family includes (names and ages):

My three best friends are:

My favorite food is:

My favorite band is:

My favorite activities are:

LOOKING AHEAD

Confirmation Day

Drivers' Licence Day

Graduation Day

When I grow up, I can hardly wait to:

One great thing I'd like to do
with my life for the world is:

Paste
SCHOOL
photo here

This is Me

Paste
FAMILY
photo here

This is My Family

FAITH INKUBATORS

Paste ancient
school photo
of your teacher
or a small
group
GUIDE
when they were
your age
here

Name

Phone

Email/IM

Birthday

One thing about me:

My Small Group Guide

Paste
SCHOOL
photo here

Name

Phone

Email/IM

Birthday

One thing about me:

My Small Group Friend

Paste
SCHOOL
photo here

Name

Phone

Email/IM

Birthday

One thing about me:

Another Friend

Paste
SCHOOL
photo here

Name

Phone

Email/IM

Birthday

One thing about me:

One More Friend

Paste
SCHOOL
photo here

Name

Phone

Email/IM

Birthday

One thing about me:

Yet Another Friend

Paste
SCHOOL
photo here

Name

Phone

Email/IM

Birthday

One thing about me:

Even One More Friend

LET THERE BE LIGHT!

In the beginning when God created the heavens and the earth, the earth was a formless void and darkness covered the face of the deep, while a wind from God swept over the face of the waters. Then God said, "Let there be..."

Listen to this song using FINKlink
BM01 @ www.faithink.com

"Light!" And there was light. And God saw that the light was good; and God called the light day and the darkness night. **Day 2:** Next God made the atmosphere and called it sky. And it was...

GOOD.

Day 3: It was time to separate the waters from the dry land, so that's just what God did. Soon the first plants began to grow and it was...

GOOD.

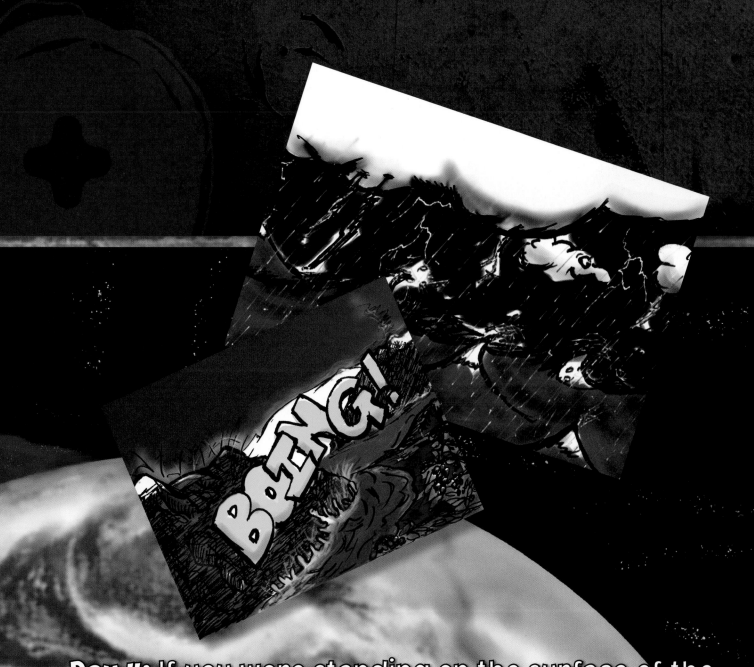

Day 4: If you were standing on the surface of the earth, the next thing you would have seen was the thick, cloudy atmosphere starting to clear. Soon the sun and moon and stars appeared and, with them, the seasons were set in place. This, too was...

GOOD.

Day 5: After that an amazing thing happened: God created life in the seas! Next birds filled the air and animals crawled onto the land. **Day 6:** Finally God created human beings. Then God took a deep, deep breath and breathed into them something none of the other animals had – a living eternal spirit. And it was...

Day 7: On the seventh day, God rested from all the creative activity. God called the seventh day holy. And God looked and saw everything and, yes, it was very, very, very, very...

GOOD. GOOD. GOOD. GOOD!

GSI (God Scene Investigation) Verse: Genesis 1:1-3
Find the hidden Bible verse in this cartoon and highlight it in your Bible. Then go to *www.faithink.com* and type in FINK*link* BM01 to learn it in song and sign language.

The Home Huddle Journal
JOURNAL

VERSE OF THE WEEK

In the beginning when God created the heavens and the earth, the earth was a formless void and darkness covered the face of the deep, while a wind from God swept over the face of the waters. Then God said, "Let there be light." And there was light... And it was very good.

Genesis 1:1-3, 31

Learn sign language for this verse using FINKlink

BM01 | @ www.faithink.com

Day 1

my **High** today was:

my **Low** today was:

my **Prayer** today is:

Day 2

my **High** today was:

my **Low** today was:

my **Prayer** today is:

Day 3

my **High** today was:

my **Low** today was:

my **Prayer** today is:

1. **Share** Highs & Lows of the day
2. **Read** sing, sign and highlight the verse of the week in your Bibles
3. **Talk** about how the verse relates to your Highs & Lows
4. **Pray** for your Highs & Lows, for your family and for the world
5. **Bless** one another using this week's blessing (bottom of next page)

Day 4

my **High** today was:

my **Low** today was:

my **Prayer** today is:

Day 5

my **High** today was:

my **Low** today was:

my **Prayer** today is:

Day 6

my **High** today was:

my **Low** today was:

my **Prayer** today is:

Art
ATTACK

Create your own artwork to help tell this week's story:

R The Week in
EVIEW

THIS WEEK'S BLESSING

(Name), child of God, may you bring the light of God to every corner of your world this day!

Looking back on the week, my highest **High** was:

....

My lowest **Low** this week was:

....

One way God answered my **Prayers** this week was:

....

One way God might use me as a **Sacred Agent** to help answer another person's prayers:

....

....

FAMILY COVENANT

Our family has shared **Highs & Lows** this week, **read** the cartoon Bible story and high-lighted the theme verse in our Bibles, **talked** about our lives, **prayed** for one another's highs and lows, and **blessed** one another.

....
Parent's Signature   **Child's Signature**   **Date**

Let There Be Light!

by Tony Axtell   Online at www.faithink.com
Genesis 1:1-3, 31

In the beginning
when God created the heavens
and the earth,
the earth was a formless void
and the darkness covered
the face of the deep

While a wind from God
swept over the face of the waters
Then God said, "Let there be light";
and there was light

And the light was very, very good
And the light was very, very,
very, very good

Let there be light! (repeat)

The Home Huddle Journal
JOURNAL

Day 1

my **High** today was:

my **Low** today was:

my **Prayer** today is:

Day 2

my **High** today was:

my **Low** today was:

my **Prayer** today is:

Day 3

my **High** today was:

my **Low** today was:

my **Prayer** today is:

1. **Share** Highs & Lows of the day
2. **Read** sing, sign and highlight the verse of the week in your Bibles
3. **Talk** about how the verse relates to your Highs & Lows
4. **Pray** for your Highs & Lows, for your family and for the world
5. **Bless** one another using this week's blessing (bottom of next page)

Day 4

my **High** today was:

my **Low** today was:

my **Prayer** today is:

Day 5

my **High** today was:

my **Low** today was:

my **Prayer** today is:

Day 6

my **High** today was:

my **Low** today was:

my **Prayer** today is:

VERSE OF THE WEEK

In the beginning when God created the heavens and the earth, the earth was a formless void and darkness covered the face of the deep, while a wind from God swept over the face of the waters. Then God said, "Let there be light." And there was light... And it was very good.

Genesis 1:1-3, 31

Learn sign language for this verse using FINKlink
BM01 | @ www.faithink.com

ARt ATTACK

Create your own artwork to help tell this week's story:

The Week in REVIEW

THIS WEEK'S BLESSING

(Name), child of God, may you bring the light of God to every corner of your world this day!

Looking back on the week, my highest **High** was:

....

My lowest **Low** this week was:

....

One way God answered my **Prayers** this week was:

....

One way God might use me as a **Sacred Agent** to help answer another person's prayers:

....

....

FAMILY COVENANT

Our family has shared **Highs & Lows** this week, **read** the cartoon Bible story and high-lighted the theme verse in our Bibles, **talked** about our lives, **prayed** for one another's highs and lows, and **blessed** one another.

....

Parent's Signature   **Child's Signature**   **Date**

Name That Verse

1. **Divide** into small groups or teams.
2. **Listen** to eight short Bible Song clips at www.faithink.com.
3. **Guess** the location of each verse. Write your answer below.
4. **Award** the following points for each correct answer:

    * **Old or New Testament**   5 points
    * **Correct Bible Book, Chapter & Verse** 10 points

5. **Record** your scores immediately in the boxes to the right.
6. **Add** subtotal of all correct answers in the box. (80 Possible)
7. **Play** Bonus Round. Get all correct and score 20 extra pts.
8. **Total** results and award prizes for added fun.

CREATION

Order this art print using FINKlink
BM01 @ www.faithink.com

Song of Solomon by He Qi www.heqiarts.com

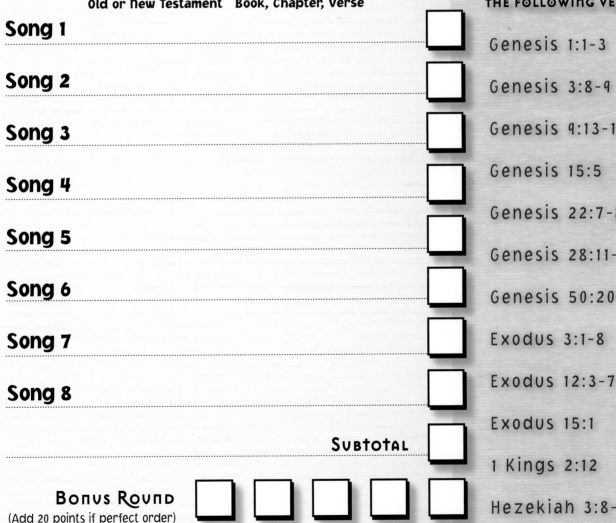

	Old or New Testament	Book, Chapter, Verse	
Song 1			☐
Song 2			☐
Song 3			☐
Song 4			☐
Song 5			☐
Song 6			☐
Song 7			☐
Song 8			☐
		Subtotal	☐

Bonus Round
(Add 20 points if perfect order) ☐ ☐ ☐ ☐ ☐

Answer Key

Choose Eight From The Following Verses

Genesis 1:1-3

Genesis 3:8-9

Genesis 9:13-14

Genesis 15:5

Genesis 22:7-8

Genesis 28:11-13

Genesis 50:20

Exodus 3:1-8

Exodus 12:3-7

Exodus 15:1

1 Kings 2:12

Hezekiah 3:8-9

Play this online game using FINKlink
BM01 @ www.faithink.com

Final Score ☐

FAITH INKUBATORS

God

set the first man and woman in a beautiful garden and told them they could run the place. "You may eat of every tree here, except the tree of the knowledge of good and evil," said God. "If you eat of that tree, you will **die!**"

Listen to this song using FINKlink
BM02 @ www.faithink.com

Things were going pretty fine until a serpent slithered down the tree one day and tempted Eve to disobey God. Eve ate of the fruit and it tasted great! She gave some to her husband. Suddenly they felt naked and ashamed. They ran and hid.

They heard the sound of the Lord God walking in the garden at the time of the evening breeze, and the man and his wife hid themselves from the presence of the Lord God among the trees of the garden. But the Lord God called to the man, and said to him...

GSI (God Scene Investigation) Verse: Genesis 3:8-9

Find the hidden Bible verse in this cartoon and highlight it in your Bible. Then go to *www.faithink.com* and type in FINK*link* BM02 to learn it in song and sign language.

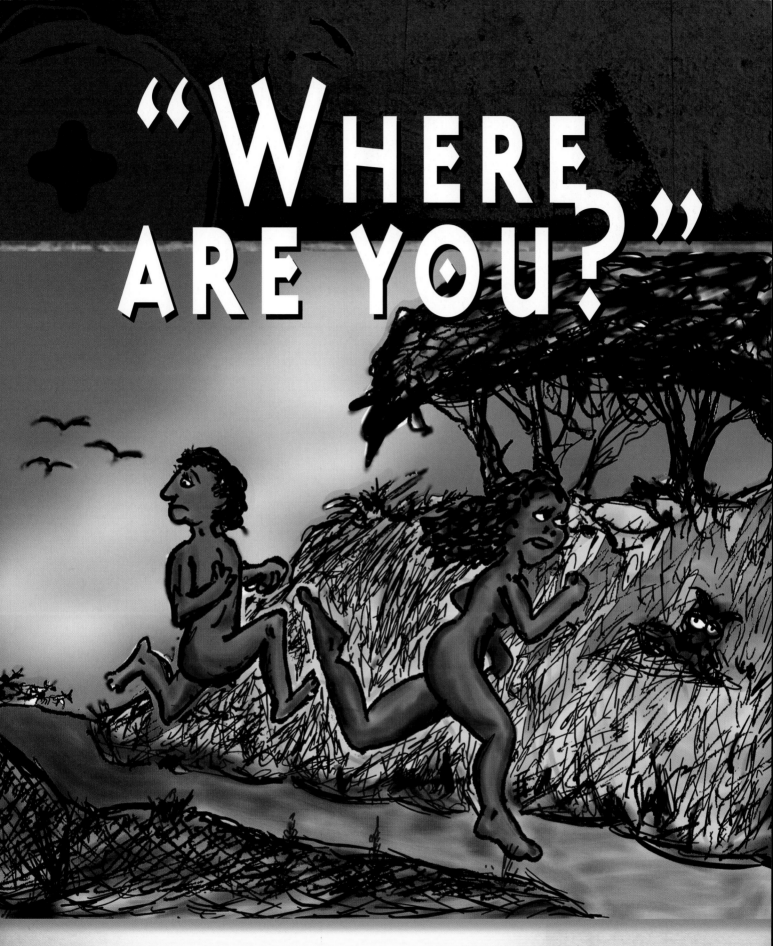

The Home Huddle Journal

journal

VERSE OF THE WEEK

They heard the sound of the Lord God walking in the garden at the time of the evening breeze, and the man and his wife hid themselves from the presence of the Lord God among the trees of the garden. But the Lord God called to the man, and said to him, "Where are you?"

Genesis 3:8-9

Learn sign language for this verse using FINKlink
BM02 @ www.faithink.com

Day 1

my **High** today was:

my **Low** today was:

my **Prayer** today is:

Day 2

my **High** today was:

my **Low** today was:

my **Prayer** today is:

Day 3

my **High** today was:

my **Low** today was:

my **Prayer** today is:

1. **Share** Highs & Lows of the day
2. **Read** sing, sign and highlight the verse of the week in your Bibles
3. **Talk** about how the verse relates to your Highs & Lows
4. **Pray** for your Highs & Lows, for your family and for the world
5. **Bless** one another using this week's blessing (bottom of next page)

Day 4

my **High** today was:

my **Low** today was:

my **Prayer** today is:

Day 5

my **High** today was:

my **Low** today was:

my **Prayer** today is:

Day 6

my **High** today was:

my **Low** today was:

my **Prayer** today is:

ART ATTACK

Create your own artwork to help tell this week's story:

The Week in REVIEW

THIS WEEK'S BLESSING

(Name), child of God, may you run toward God and not away, every day in every way.

Looking back on the week, my highest **High** was:

....

My lowest **Low** this week was:

....

One way God answered my **Prayers** this week was:

....

One way God might use me as a **Sacred Agent** to help answer another person's prayers:

....

....

FAMILY COVENANT

Our family has shared **Highs & Lows** this week, **read** the cartoon Bible story and high-lighted the theme verse in our Bibles, **talked** about our lives, **prayed** for one another's highs and lows, and **blessed** one another.

....
Parent's Signature   **Child's Signature**   **Date**

Where Are You?

by Agapé   Online at www.faithink.com
Genesis 3:8-9

Genesis 3, Genesis 3, Genesis 3:8 and 9
Where are you? Where are you?
Where are you? Where are you? (repeat)

They heard (repeat) the sound (repeat)
of the Lord God walking in the garden
They heard (repeat) the sound (repeat)
of the Lord God walking in the garden

At the time of the evening breeze (repeat)
At the time of the evening breeze (repeat)

And the man and his wife (repeat)
hid themselves from the presence of the Lord
And the man and his wife (repeat)
hid themselves from the presence of the Lord

God among the trees of the garden (repeat)
God among the trees of the garden (repeat)

But the Lord God called to
the man and said to him, "Where are you?"
But the Lord God called to the man
and said to him, "Where are you?" (repeat)

Where are you? (repeat)

Listen to this song using FINKlink
BM02 @ www.faithink.com

The Home Huddle Journal
JOURNAL

Day 1

my **High** today was:

my **Low** today was:

my **Prayer** today is:

Day 2

my **High** today was:

my **Low** today was:

my **Prayer** today is:

Day 3

my **High** today was:

my **Low** today was:

my **Prayer** today is:

1. **Share** Highs & Lows of the day
2. **Read** sing, sign and highlight the verse of the week in your Bibles
3. **Talk** about how the verse relates to your Highs & Lows
4. **Pray** for your Highs & Lows, for your family and for the world
5. **Bless** one another using this week's blessing (bottom of next page)

Day 4

my **High** today was:

my **Low** today was:

my **Prayer** today is:

Day 5

my **High** today was:

my **Low** today was:

my **Prayer** today is:

Day 6

my **High** today was:

my **Low** today was:

my **Prayer** today is:

VERSE OF THE WEEK

They heard the sound of the Lord God walking in the garden at the time of the evening breeze, and the man and his wife hid themselves from the presence of the Lord God among the trees of the garden. But the Lord God called to the man, and said to him, "Where are you?"

Genesis 3:8-9

Learn sign language for this verse using FINKlink

BM02 | @ www.faithink.com

ART ATTACK

Create your own artwork to help tell this week's story:

The Week in REVIEW

Looking back on the week, my highest **High** was:

....

My lowest **Low** this week was:

....

One way God answered my **Prayers** this week was:

....

One way God might use me as a **Sacred Agent** to help answer another person's prayers:

....

....

FAMILY COVENANT

Our family has shared **Highs & Lows** this week, **read** the cartoon Bible story and high-lighted the theme verse in our Bibles, **talked** about our lives, **prayed** for one another's highs and lows, and **blessed** one another.

....
Parent's Signature   **Child's Signature**   **Date**

Name That Verse

1. **Divide** into small groups or teams.
2. **Listen** to eight short Bible Song clips at www.faithink.com.
3. **Guess** the location of each verse. Write your answer below.
4. **Award** the following points for each correct answer:

   * **Old or New Testament**   5 points
   * **Correct Bible Book, Chapter & Verse**   10 points

5. **Record** your scores immediately in the boxes to the right.
6. **Add** subtotal of all correct answers in the box. (80 Possible)
7. **Play** Bonus Round. Get all correct and score 20 extra pts.
8. **Total** results and award prizes for added fun.

Losing paradise by He Qi
www.heqiarts.com

Order this art print using FINKlink
BM02 @ www.faithink.com

Order this art print using FINKlink
BM02 @ www.faithink.com

	Old or New Testament	Book, Chapter, Verse	
Song 1			☐
Song 2			☐
Song 3			☐
Song 4			☐
Song 5			☐
Song 6			☐
Song 7			☐
Song 8			☐
		Subtotal	☐

Answer Key
Choose eight from the following verses

Genesis 1:1-3

Genesis 3:8-9

Genesis 9:13-14

Genesis 15:5

Genesis 28:11-13

Genesis 50:20

Exodus 3:1-8

Exodus 15:1

1 Kings 2:12

Proverbs 15:16

Daniel 16:16b

John 3:16

Bonus Round
(Add 20 points if perfect order)
☐ ☐ ☐ ☐ ☐

Play this online game using FINKlink
BM02 @ www.faithink.com

Play this online game using FINKlink
BM02 @ www.faithink.com

Final Score ☐

FAITH INKUBATORS

Something

had gone terribly wrong in God's perfect world. When Adam and Eve sinned, pain and death entered the scene. Their first son, Cain, killed his brother, Abel. As the human race spread across the face of the earth, hatred, jealousy and death spread with them. Finally God had enough. "I am sorry I made them!" said the Lord. "I am starting over!"

Listen to this song using FINKlink
BM03 @ www.faithink.com

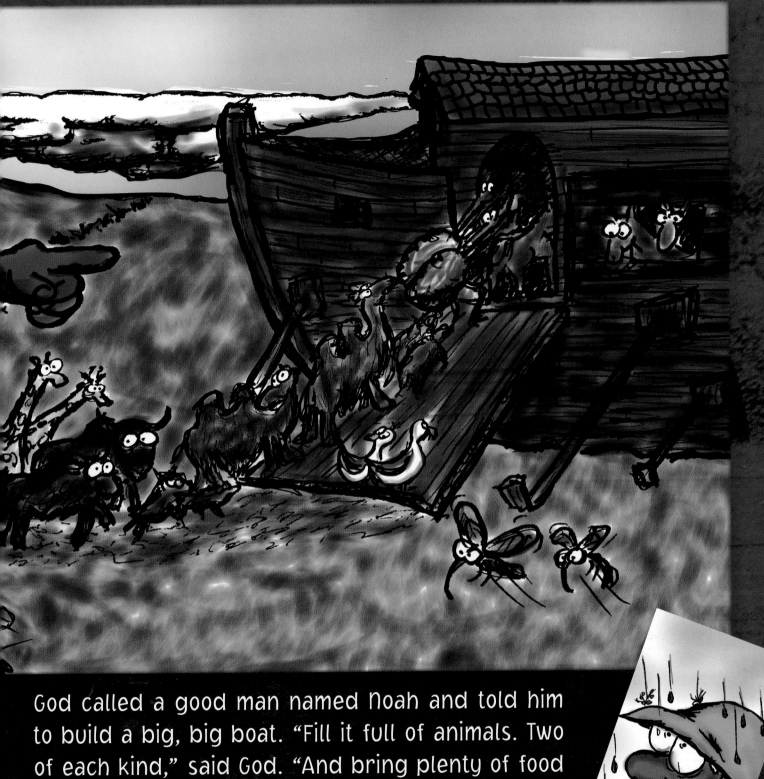

God called a good man named Noah and told him to build a big, big boat. "Fill it full of animals. Two of each kind," said God. "And bring plenty of food for them and for your family!" Noah did as God commanded. He built an ark and filled it with animals. Then it began to rain... and rain... and rain...

and rain... and rain...

For forty days and forty nights it rained. A great flood covered the earth and everything died. But Noah, his family, and all of the animals were safe and sound in the ark. Finally the rain stopped, the floods drained away and a beautiful rainbow was seen in the clouds. God gave the rainbow as a sign that the world would never again be destroyed by a flood. "I have set my bow in the clouds..."

COVENANT
between me and the earth."

"When I see clouds over the earth and the bow is seen in the clouds, I will **remember my covenant** that is between me and you. And you, be fruitful and multiply. Abound on the earth and multiply in it."

GSI (God Scene Investigation) Verse: Genesis 9:13-15a

Find the hidden Bible verse in this cartoon and highlight it in your Bible. Then go to *www.faithink.com* and type in FINK*link* BM03 to learn it in song and sign language.

God gave Noah a promise along with the rainbow:

"As long as the earth endures, seedtime and harvest, cold and heat, summer and winter, day and night shall not cease."

And God blessed Noah and his family, and they spread across the face of the earth.

The Home Huddle Journal
Journal

VERSE OF THE WEEK

I have set my bow in the clouds and it will be a sign of the covenant between me and the earth. When I see clouds over the earth and the bow is seen in the clouds, I will remember my covenant that is between me and you.

Genesis 9:13-15a

Day 1

my **High** today was:

my **Low** today was:

my **Prayer** today is:

Day 2

my **High** today was:

my **Low** today was:

my **Prayer** today is:

Day 3

my **High** today was:

my **Low** today was:

my **Prayer** today is:

Learn sign language for this verse using FINKlink

BM03 | @ www.faithink.com

1. **Share** Highs & Lows of the day
2. **Read** sing, sign and highlight the verse of the week in your Bibles
3. **Talk** about how the verse relates to your Highs & Lows
4. **Pray** for your Highs & Lows, for your family and for the world
5. **Bless** one another using this week's blessing (bottom of next page)

Day 4

my **High** today was:

my **Low** today was:

my **Prayer** today is:

Day 5

my **High** today was:

my **Low** today was:

my **Prayer** today is:

Day 6

my **High** today was:

my **Low** today was:

my **Prayer** today is:

ART
ATTACK

DRAW A PICTURE!

Create your own artwork to help tell this week's story:

The Week in REVIEW

THIS WEEK'S BLESSING

(Name), child of God, may God rescue you from all the floods of life.

Looking back on the week, my highest **High** was:

....

My lowest **Low** this week was:

....

One way God answered my **Prayers** this week was:

....

One way God might use me as a **Sacred Agent** to help answer another person's prayers:

....

....

FAMILY COVENANT

Our family has shared **Highs & Lows** this week, **read** the cartoon Bible story and high-lighted the theme verse in our Bibles, **talked** about our lives, **prayed** for one another's highs and lows, and **blessed** one another.

_____   _____   _____
Parent's Signature   **Child's Signature**   **Date**

Bow in the Clouds

by Rich Melheim   Online at www.faithink.com
Genesis 9:7, 13, 14, 15a, 22

I have set my bow in the clouds
and it shall be a sign
A sign of the covenant
between me and the earth
When I bring clouds over the earth
and the bow is seen in the clouds
I have set my bow in the clouds
and it shall be a sign

I will remember my covenant that is
between me and you
And you, be fruitful and multiply
Abound on the earth and multiply in it

As long as the earth endures
seedtime and harvest,
cold and heat, summer and winter,
day and night shall not cease

Listen to this song using FINKlink
BM03 | @ www.faithink.com

The Home Huddle Journal
JOURNAL

Week 2 (use this if you're doing a theme every 2 weeks)

Day 1

my **High** today was:

my **Low** today was:

my **Prayer** today is:

Day 2

my **High** today was:

my **Low** today was:

my **Prayer** today is:

Day 3

my **High** today was:

my **Low** today was:

my **Prayer** today is:

1. **Share** Highs & Lows of the day
2. **Read** sing, sign and highlight the verse of the week in your Bibles
3. **Talk** about how the verse relates to your Highs & Lows
4. **Pray** for your Highs & Lows, for your family and for the world
5. **Bless** one another using this week's blessing (bottom of next page)

Day 4

my **High** today was:

my **Low** today was:

my **Prayer** today is:

Day 5

my **High** today was:

my **Low** today was:

my **Prayer** today is:

Day 6

my **High** today was:

my **Low** today was:

my **Prayer** today is:

VERSE OF THE WEEK

I have set my bow in the clouds and it will be a sign of the covenant between me and the earth. When I see clouds over the earth and the bow is seen in the clouds, I will remember my covenant that is between me and you.

Genesis 9:13-15a

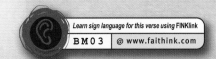

Learn sign language for this verse using FINKlink

BM03 @ www.faithink.com

ART ATTACK

Create your own artwork to help tell this week's story:

The Week in REVIEW

THIS WEEK'S BLESSING

(Name), child of God, may God rescue you from all the floods of life.

Looking back on the week, my highest **High** was:

My lowest **Low** this week was:

One way God answered my **Prayers** this week was:

One way God might use me as a **Sacred Agent** to help answer another person's prayers:

FAMILY COVENANT

Our family has shared **Highs & Lows** this week, **read** the cartoon Bible story and highlighted the theme verse in our Bibles, **talked** about our lives, **prayed** for one another's highs and lows, and **blessed** one another.

....
Parent's Signature   Child's Signature   Date

Name that Verse

1. **Divide** into small groups or teams.
2. **Listen** to eight short Bible Song clips at www.faithink.com.
3. **Guess** the location of each verse. Write your answer below.
4. **Award** the following points for each correct answer:

   * **Old or New Testament**   5 points
   * **Correct Bible Book, Chapter & Verse**   10 points

5. **Record** your scores immediately in the boxes to the right.
6. **Add** subtotal of all correct answers in the box. (80 Possible)
7. **Play** Bonus Round. Get all correct and score 20 extra pts.
8. **Total** results and award prizes for added fun.

Ark of Noah by He Qi
www.HEQIARTS.com

Order this art print using FINKlink
BM03 @ www.faithink.com

Old or New Testament   Book, Chapter, Verse

Song 1

Song 2

Song 3

Song 4

Song 5

Song 6

Song 7

Song 8

Subtotal

Bonus Round
(Add 20 points if perfect order)

Final Score

Answer Key

Choose eight from the following verses

Genesis 3:8-9

Genesis 9:13-14

Genesis 15:5

Genesis 22:7-8

Genesis 50:20

Exodus 12:3-7

Exodus 15:1

Psalm 23:1

Proverbs 15:16

Daniel 16:16b

Jonah 2:1-2

2 Corinthians 5:17

Play this online game using FINKlink
BM03 @ www.faithink.com

FAITH INKUBATORS

STORY
no | 4

Long

ago God called an old childless couple to leave their home and family and travel to a new land. If they would make this journey of faith, God promised to give them a land of their own and to bless the whole world through their children and grandchildren.

Listen to this song using FINKlink
BM04 | @ www.faithink.com

Abraham and his wife Sarah packed up and left for the Promised Land, but 25 years passed, and still no baby!

NO BABY!
NO BABY!
NO BABY!

NO BABY!
OH BABY!
NO BABY!

NO BABY!
NO BABY!
NO BABY!

GSI (God Scene Investigation) Verse: Genesis 15:5
Find the hidden Bible verse in this cartoon and highlight it in your Bible. Then go to *www.faithink.com* and type in FINK*link* BM04 to learn it in song and sign language.

NO BABY! NO BABY! NO BABY!

Then one night the Lord came to Abraha
in a vision. "Do not be afraid... I am you
shield. Your reward shall be very great
Abraham asked, "Oh Lord God, what wil
you give me? For I continue childless!"

God brought old Abraham out to look at the
NIGHT SKY.

"Look toward the heaven and count the stars, if you are able to count them. So shall your descendants be. I will establish my covenant between me and you and your offspring throughout their generations, to be God to you and to your offspring."

And Abraham believed the Lord.

And the Lord reckoned it to him as righteousness. Abraham was **100 years** old when his son Isaac was born to him. Sarah said: "God has brought laughter for me. Everyone who **hears will...**

LAUGH!

VERSE OF THE WEEK

Look toward the heaven and count the stars, if you are able to count them. So shall your descendants be.

Genesis 15:5

Day 1

my **High** today was:

my **Low** today was:

my **Prayer** today is:

Day 2

my **High** today was:

my **Low** today was:

my **Prayer** today is:

Day 3

my **High** today was:

my **Low** today was:

my **Prayer** today is:

Learn sign language for this verse using FINKlink
BM04 | @ www.faithink.com

1. **Share** Highs & Lows of the day
2. **Read** sing, sign and highlight the verse of the week in your Bibles
3. **Talk** about how the verse relates to your Highs & Lows
4. **Pray** for your Highs & Lows, for your family and for the world
5. **Bless** one another using this week's blessing (bottom of next page)

Day 4

my **High** today was:

my **Low** today was:

my **Prayer** today is:

Day 5

my **High** today was:

my **Low** today was:

my **Prayer** today is:

Day 6

my **High** today was:

my **Low** today was:

my **Prayer** today is:

ART ATTACK

Create your own artwork to help tell this week's story:

The Week in REVIEW

THIS WEEK'S BLESSING

(Name), child of God, may you always follow where the Good Lord leads.

Looking back on the week, my highest **High** was:

....

My lowest **Low** this week was:

....

One way God answered my **Prayers** this week was:

....

One way God might use me as a **Sacred Agent** to help answer another person's prayers:

....

....

FAMILY COVENANT

Our family has shared **Highs & Lows** this week, **read** the cartoon Bible story and highlighted the theme verse in our Bibles, **talked** about our lives, **prayed** for one another's highs and lows, and **blessed** one another.

....

Parent's Signature   **Child's Signature**   **Date**

Look Toward the Heaven

by Rich Melheim   Online at www.faithink.com
Genesis 15:1-2, 5b-6, 17:7, 21:5-6

Look toward the heaven and count the stars
if you are able to count them
So shall your descendants be
So shall your descendants be
1-2-3-4

The Lord came to Abraham in a vision:
"Do not be afraid, I am your shield;
your reward shall be very great!"
"Oh Lord God, what will you give me,
for I continue childless?"

"I will establish my covenant between me and you
and your offspring through their generations,
to be God to you and to your offspring
throughout their generations"

(spoken)
And he believed the Lord
and the Lord reckoned it to him as righteousness
Abraham was 100 years old when his son
Isaac was born to him
Sarah said, "God has brought laughter for me,
everyone who hears will laugh!"

Look! Look! Look! (etc.)

Listen to this song using FINKlink
BM04 @ www.faithink.com

The Home Huddle Journal

jOURNAL

Week 2 (Use this if you're doing a theme every 2 weeks)

Day 1

my **High** today was:

my **Low** today was:

my **Prayer** today is:

Day 2

my **High** today was:

my **Low** today was:

my **Prayer** today is:

Day 3

my **High** today was:

my **Low** today was:

my **Prayer** today is:

1. **Share** Highs & Lows of the day
2. **Read** sing, sign and highlight the verse of the week in your Bibles
3. **Talk** about how the verse relates to your Highs & Lows
4. **Pray** for your Highs & Lows, for your family and for the world
5. **Bless** one another using this week's blessing (bottom of next page)

Day 4

my **High** today was:

my **Low** today was:

my **Prayer** today is:

Day 5

my **High** today was:

my **Low** today was:

my **Prayer** today is:

Day 6

my **High** today was:

my **Low** today was:

my **Prayer** today is:

VERSE OF THE WEEK

Look toward the heaven and count the stars, if you are able to count them. So shall your descendants be.

Genesis 15:5

Learn sign language for this verse using FINKlink
BM04 @ www.faithink.com

ART ATTACK

Create your own artwork to help tell this week's story:

R The Week² in EVIEW

†HIS WEEK'S BLESSING

(Name), child of God, may you always follow where the Good Lord leads.

Looking back on the week, my highest **High** was:

....

My lowest **Low** this week was:

....

One way God answered my **Prayers** this week was:

....

One way God might use me as a **Sacred Agent** to help answer another person's prayers:

....

....

FAMILY COVENANT

Our family has shared **Highs & Lows** this week, **read** the cartoon Bible story and high-lighted the theme verse in our Bibles, **talked** about our lives, **prayed** for one another's highs and lows, and **blessed** one another.

....

Parent's Signature   **Child's Signature**   **Date**

Name That Verse

Look toward the Heaven by He Qi www.HEQIARTS.com

Order this art print using FINKlink
BM04 @ www.faithink.com

1. **Divide** into small groups or teams.
2. **Listen** to eight short Bible Song clips at www.faithink.com.
3. **Guess** the location of each verse. Write your answer below.
4. **Award** the following points for each correct answer:

   * **Old or New Testament**   5 points
   * **Correct Bible Book, Chapter & Verse**   10 points

5. **Record** your scores immediately in the boxes to the right.
6. **Add** subtotal of all correct answers in the box. (80 Possible)
7. **Play** Bonus Round. Get all correct and score 20 extra pts.
8. **Total** results and award prizes for added fun.

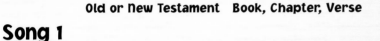

	Old or New Testament	Book, Chapter, Verse	

ANSWER KEY
CHOOSE EIGHT FROM THE FOLLOWING VERSES

Song 1 ☐   Genesis 1:1-3

Song 2 ☐   Genesis 3:8-9

Song 3 ☐   Genesis 9:13-14

Song 4 ☐   Genesis 15:5

Song 5 ☐   Genesis 22:7-8

Song 6 ☐   Genesis 28:11-13

Song 7 ☐   Genesis 50:20

Song 8 ☐   Exodus 3:1-8

Subtotal ☐   Psalm 23:1-6

Matthew 1:1-3

Mark 1:1-3

BONUS ROUND ☐ ☐ ☐ ☐ ☐   John 1:1-3
(Add 20 points if perfect order)

Play this online game using FINKlink
BM04 @ www.faithink.com

FINAL SCORE ☐

FAITH INKUBATORS

God

tested Abraham saying, "Take your son, your only son Isaac, whom you love, and go to the land of Moriah and offer him there as a burnt offering on one of the mountains that I shall show you."

Listen to this song using FINKlink
BM05 | @ www.faithink.com

So Abraham rose early in the morning, cut the wood and laid it on his son. And he, himself, carried the fire and the knife. And Isaac said:

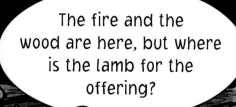

The fire and the wood are here, but where is the lamb for the offering?

God, himself, will provide the lamb for the burnt offering, my son.

Then Abraham built an altar, bound his son and laid him on top of the wood. He reached out his hand and took the knife.

But an angel called: "Abraham!" He said, "Here I am." "Do not lay a hand on the boy, for now I know that you fear God." And Abraham looked up and saw a ram caught in a thicket by its horns. He took the ram and offered it up instead of his son. So Abraham called the place "The Lord will provide"; as it is said to this day...

GSI (God Scene Investigation) Verse: Genesis 22:8a, 13-14

Find the hidden Bible verse in this cartoon and highlight it in your Bible. Then go to *www.faithink.com* and type in FINK*link* BM05 to learn it in song and sign language.

"On the mount of the Lord it shall be provided."

The Home Huddle Journal

jOURNAL

VERSE OF THE WEEK

God, himself, will provide the lamb for the burnt offering, my son.

-Genesis 22:8

Day 1

my **High** today was:

my **Low** today was:

my **Prayer** today is:

Day 2

my **High** today was:

my **Low** today was:

my **Prayer** today is:

Day 3

my **High** today was:

my **Low** today was:

my **Prayer** today is:

Learn sign language for this verse using FINKlink

BM05 | @ www.faithink.com

1. **Share** Highs & Lows of the day
2. **Read** sing, sign and highlight the verse of the week in your Bibles
3. **Talk** about how the verse relates to your Highs & Lows
4. **Pray** for your Highs & Lows, for your family and for the world
5. **Bless** one another using this week's blessing (bottom of next page)

Day 4

my **High** today was:

my **Low** today was:

my **Prayer** today is:

Day 5

my **High** today was:

my **Low** today was:

my **Prayer** today is:

Day 6

my **High** today was:

my **Low** today was:

my **Prayer** today is:

 **ART ATTACK**

Create your own artwork to help tell this week's story:

 **R The Week in REVIEW**

THIS WEEK'S BLESSING

(Name), child of God, may God provide your every need.

Looking back on the week, my highest **High** was:

My lowest **Low** this week was:

One way God answered my **Prayers** this week was:

One way God might use me as a **Sacred Agent** to help answer another person's prayers:

FAMILY COVENANT

Our family has shared **Highs & Lows** this week, **read** the cartoon Bible story and high-lighted the theme verse in our Bibles, **talked** about our lives, **prayed** for one another's highs and lows, and **blessed** one another.

_____   _____   _____
Parent's Signature   **Child's Signature**   **Date**

God Will Provide

by Rich Melheim   Online at www.faithink.com
Genesis 22:2-3, 6-9, 11-14 & John 1:29

(Boys) Ya ya Yahweh, Ya ya Yahweh, Ya ya Yahweh, Ya ya Yahweh (repeat)
(Girls) God himself will provide the lamb
for the burnt offering, my son, yeah
God himself will provide the lamb

God will provide, God will provide the lamb for the burnt offering, my son, yeah
God will provide, God will provide the lamb
Isaac said, "The fire and the wood are here,
but where is the lamb for the offering, where?"
God will provide, God will provide the lamb

God tested Abraham, said "Take your son, your only son, Isaac, whom you love
and go to the land of Moriah and offer him there
as a burnt offering on one of the mountains that I'll show you
Take your son, your only son and offer him there."

So Abraham rose early in the morning, cut the wood and laid it on his son
And he, himself, carried the fire and the kni-i-i-ife
Isaac said, "The fire and the wood are here,
but where is the lamb for the offering, where?"
Abraham stopped, and this is what he said:

God will provide, God will provide, the lamb for the burnt offering, my son, yeah
God will provide, God will provide the lamb"
Isaac said, "The fire and the wood are here,
but where is the lamb for the offering, where?"
God will provide, God will provide the lamb

Abraham built an altar, bound his son and laid him on top of the wood
Reached out his hand and took the kni-i-i-ife
But the angel called, "Abraham!" "Here I am."
"Do not lay a hand on the boy, not a hand
For now I know that you fear God, do not lay a hand."

God will provide...

And Abraham looked up and saw a ram caught in a thicket by its horns
and took the ram and offered it up instead of his son, his only son
So Abraham called that place "The Lord will provide"
as it said to this day, "On the mount of the Lord it shall be provided"
On the mount of the Lord it shall be...

God will provide...

Behold the Lamb of God who takes
Behold the Lamb of God who takes the sin of the world away

Listen to this song using **FINKlink**
BM05 | @ www.faithink.com

Day 1

my **High** today was:

my **Low** today was:

my **Prayer** today is:

Day 2

my **High** today was:

my **Low** today was:

my **Prayer** today is:

Day 3

my **High** today was:

my **Low** today was:

my **Prayer** today is:

1. **Share** Highs & Lows of the day
2. **Read** sing, sign and highlight the verse of the week in your Bibles
3. **Talk** about how the verse relates to your Highs & Lows
4. **Pray** for your Highs & Lows, for your family and for the world
5. **Bless** one another using this week's blessing (bottom of next page)

Day 4

my **High** today was:

my **Low** today was:

my **Prayer** today is:

Day 5

my **High** today was:

my **Low** today was:

my **Prayer** today is:

Day 6

my **High** today was:

my **Low** today was:

my **Prayer** today is:

VERSE OF THE WEEK

God, himself, will provide the lamb for the burnt offering, my son.

-Genesis 22:8

Learn sign language for this verse using FINKlink

BM05 | @ www.faithink.com

ART ATTACK

Create your own artwork to help tell this week's story:

The Week in REVIEW

Looking back on the week, my highest **High** was:

....

My lowest **Low** this week was:

....

One way God answered my **Prayers** this week was:

....

THIS WEEK'S BLESSING

(Name), child of God, may God provide your every need.

One way God might use me as a **Sacred Agent** to help answer another person's prayers:

....

....

FAMILY COVENANT

Our family has shared **Highs & Lows** this week, **read** the cartoon Bible story and highlighted the theme verse in our Bibles, **talked** about our lives, **prayed** for one another's highs and lows, and **blessed** one another.

----------------------------   ----------------------------   ----------------
Parent's Signature   **Child's Signature**   **Date**

Name That Verse

1. **Divide** into small groups or teams.
2. **Listen** to eight short Bible Song clips at www.faithink.com.
3. **Guess** the location of each verse. Write your answer below.
4. **Award** the following points for each correct answer:

   * **Old or New Testament**   5 points
   * **Correct Bible Book, Chapter & Verse**   10 points

5. **Record** your scores immediately in the boxes to the right.
6. **Add** subtotal of all correct answers in the box. (80 Possible)
7. **Play** Bonus Round. Get all correct and score 20 extra pts.
8. **Total** results and award prizes for added fun.

Sacrifice of Abraham by He Qi

www.HEQiARTS.com

Order this art print using FINKlink
BM05 @ www.faithink.com

Answer Key

CHOOSE EIGHT FROM THE FOLLOWING VERSES

	Old or New Testament	Book, Chapter, Verse	
Song 1			
Song 2			
Song 3			
Song 4			
Song 5			
Song 6			
Song 7			
Song 8			
		Subtotal	

Genesis 1:1 - 3

Genesis 9:13-14

Genesis 15:5

Genesis 22:7-8

Genesis 28:11-13

Exodus 3:1-8

Exodus 12:3-7

Exodus 31:8

Hezekiah 4:44

Matthew 1:13-16

Matthew 5:13-16

Matthew 51:3-16

BONUS ROUND
(Add 20 points if perfect order)

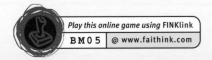

Play this online game using FINKlink
BM05 @ www.faithink.com

FINAL SCORE

FAITH INKUBATORS

Jacob

was born hanging onto his twin, trying to pull his brother Esau down by the heel. The grandsons of old Abraham and Sarah were as different as night and day, and were destined to compete. Esau was strong as a bull and covered with red hair. He loved to hunt with his father, Isaac. Jacob was handsome, but shrewd. His mother, Rebekah, always liked him best.

Listen to this song using FINKlink
BM06 @ www.faithink.com

The rivalry between the boys grew as they did.
Once, when Esau returned from a hunt empty-handed,
Jacob was cooking a delicious stew.

When Esau realized what he had
done, he was very, very angry.

*The largest share of inheritance reserved for the firstborn son.

Years later, when Isaac was old and nearly blind, he called his firstborn son Esau to make him a special meal of wild game. Rebekah overheard this. While Esau was out on the hunt, she told Jacob to fix a meal and bring it to his father. Disguised as his brother...

GSI (God Scene Investigation) Verse: Genesis 28:11-14

Find the hidden Bible verse in this cartoon and highlight it in your Bible. Then go to *www.faithink.com* and type in FINK*link* BM06 to learn it in song and sign language.

...Isaac gave Jake the blessing by **mistake!**
Jacob was now on the

run for his life.

I'm gonna **kill** you!

Jacob came to a certain place and he stayed there for the night because the sun had set. Taking one of the stones of the place, he put it under his head and lay down in that place.

And he dreamed that there was a ladder set up on the earth, the top of it reaching to heaven and the angels of God were ascending and descending on it. And the Lord stood beside him and said:

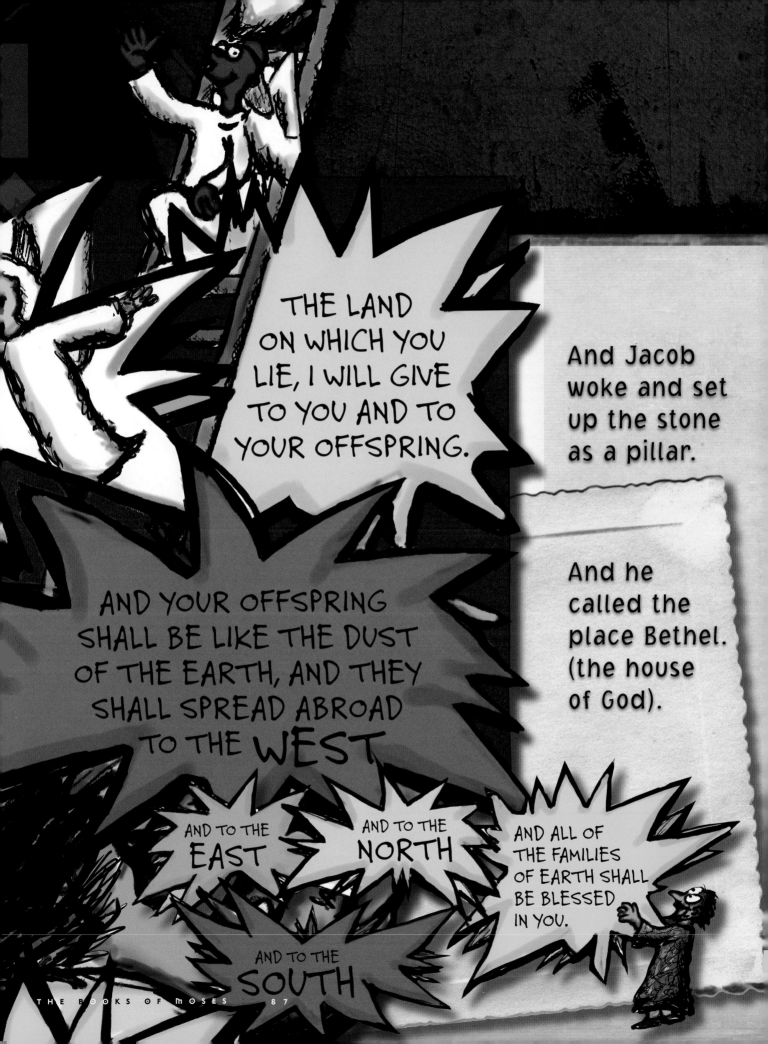

The Home Huddle Journal
JOURNAL

VERSE OF THE WEEK

He (Jacob) came to a certain place and stayed there for the night, because the sun had set. Taking one of the stones of the place, he put it under his head and lay down in that place. And he dreamed that there was a ladder set up on the earth...

Genesis 28:11-12

Day 1

my **High** today was:

my **Low** today was:

my **Prayer** today is:

Day 2

my **High** today was:

my **Low** today was:

my **Prayer** today is:

Day 3

my **High** today was:

my **Low** today was:

my **Prayer** today is:

Learn sign language for this verse using FINKlink
BM06 | @ www.faithink.com

1. **Share** Highs & Lows of the day
2. **Read** sing, sign and highlight the verse of the week in your Bibles
3. **Talk** about how the verse relates to your Highs & Lows
4. **Pray** for your Highs & Lows, for your family and for the world
5. **Bless** one another using this week's blessing (bottom of next page)

Day 4

my **High** today was:

my **Low** today was:

my **Prayer** today is:

Day 5

my **High** today was:

my **Low** today was:

my **Prayer** today is:

Day 6

my **High** today was:

my **Low** today was:

my **Prayer** today is:

Art ATTACK

Create your own artwork to help tell this week's story:

The Week in Review

Looking back on the week, my highest **High** was:

....

My lowest **Low** this week was:

....

This Week's Blessing

(Name), child of God, may God's holy angels watch over you this day in all you do and all you say.

One way God answered my **Prayers** this week was:

....

One way God might use me as a **Sacred Agent** to help answer another person's prayers:

....

....

Family Covenant

Our family has shared **Highs & Lows** this week, **read** the cartoon Bible story and highlighted the theme verse in our Bibles, **talked** about our lives, **prayed** for one another's highs and lows, and **blessed** one another.

....

Parent's Signature   **Child's Signature**   **Date**

Jake's Dream

by Rich Melheim Online at www.faithink.com
Genesis 28:11-14

Jacob came to a certain place
and he stayed there for the night
because the sun had set
because the sun had set

Taking one of the stones of the place
he put it under his head and lay
down in that place
And he dreamed that there was a ladder
set up on the earth

The top of it reaching to heaven
and the angels of God were ascending
and descending on it
and the Lord stood beside him and said:

"I am the Lord your God
the God of Abraham your father
and the God of Isaac
The land on which you lie
I will give to you and to your offspring
And your offspring shall be
like the dust of the earth
and you shall spread abroad to the west
and to the east and to the north
and to the south
and all the families of the earth
shall be blessed in you"

"I am the Lord your God
the God of Abraham your father
and the God of Isaac"

The Home Huddle Journal
Journal

Week 2 (Use this if you're doing a theme every 2 weeks)

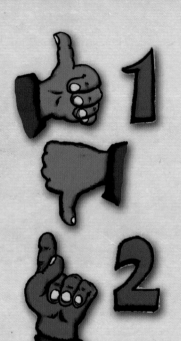

Day 1

my **High** today was:

my **Low** today was:

my **Prayer** today is:

Day 2

my **High** today was:

my **Low** today was:

my **Prayer** today is:

Day 3

my **High** today was:

my **Low** today was:

my **Prayer** today is:

1. **Share** Highs & Lows of the day
2. **Read** sing, sign and highlight the verse of the week in your Bibles
3. **Talk** about how the verse relates to your Highs & Lows
4. **Pray** for your Highs & Lows, for your family and for the world
5. **Bless** one another using this week's blessing (bottom of next page)

Day 4

my **High** today was:

my **Low** today was:

my **Prayer** today is:

Day 5

my **High** today was:

my **Low** today was:

my **Prayer** today is:

Day 6

my **High** today was:

my **Low** today was:

my **Prayer** today is:

VERSE OF THE WEEK

He (Jacob) came to a certain place and stayed there for the night, because the sun had set. Taking one of the stones of the place, he put it under his head and lay down in that place. And he dreamed that there was a ladder set up on the earth...

Genesis 28:11-12

Learn sign language for this verse using FINKlink
BM06 @ www.faithink.com

ART ATTACK

Create your own artwork to help tell this week's story:

The Week in REVIEW

Looking back on the week, my highest **High** was:

....

My lowest **Low** this week was:

....

One way God answered my **Prayers** this week was:

....

One way God might use me as a **Sacred Agent** to help answer another person's prayers:

....

....

FAMILY COVENANT

Our family has shared **Highs & Lows** this week, **read** the cartoon Bible story and highlighted the theme verse in our Bibles, **talked** about our lives, **prayed** for one another's highs and lows, and **blessed** one another.

_____   _____   _____
Parent's Signature   Child's Signature   Date

Name That Verse

1. **Divide** into small groups or teams.
2. **Listen** to eight short Bible Song clips at www.faithink.com.
3. **Guess** the location of each verse. Write your answer below.
4. **Award** the following points for each correct answer:

   * **Old or New Testament**   5 points
   * **Correct Bible Book, Chapter & Verse** 10 points

5. **Record** your scores immediately in the boxes to the right.
6. **Add** subtotal of all correct answers in the box. (80 Possible)
7. **Play** Bonus Round. Get all correct and score 20 extra pts.
8. **Total** results and award prizes for added fun.

JACOB'S DREAM BY HEQI
www.HEQIARTS.com

Order this art print using FINKlink
BM06 @ www.faithink.com

ANSWER KEY

CHOOSE EIGHT FROM THE FOLLOWING VERSES

GENESIS 1:1-3

GENESIS 9:13-14

GENESIS 15:5

GENESIS 22:7-8

GENESIS 28:11-14

GENESIS 50:20

EXODUS 3:1-8

NUMBERS 6:24-26

LEVITICUS 6:24-26

MATTHEW 6:9-11

MATTHEW 69:11

MATTHEW 691:1

	Old or New Testament	Book, Chapter, Verse	
Song 1			☐
Song 2			☐
Song 3			☐
Song 4			☐
Song 5			☐
Song 6			☐
Song 7			☐
Song 8			☐
		Subtotal	☐

BONUS ROUND
(Add 20 points if perfect order)   ☐ ☐ ☐ ☐ ☐

Play this online game using FINKlink
BM06 @ www.faithink.com

FINAL SCORE ☐

FAITH INKUBATORS

God

blessed Jacob with a new name—Israel—and with twelve sons. Now Israel loved Joseph more than any other of his children, because he was the son of his old age. And he had made him a coat of many colors.

Listen to this song using FINKlink
BM07 @ www.faithink.com

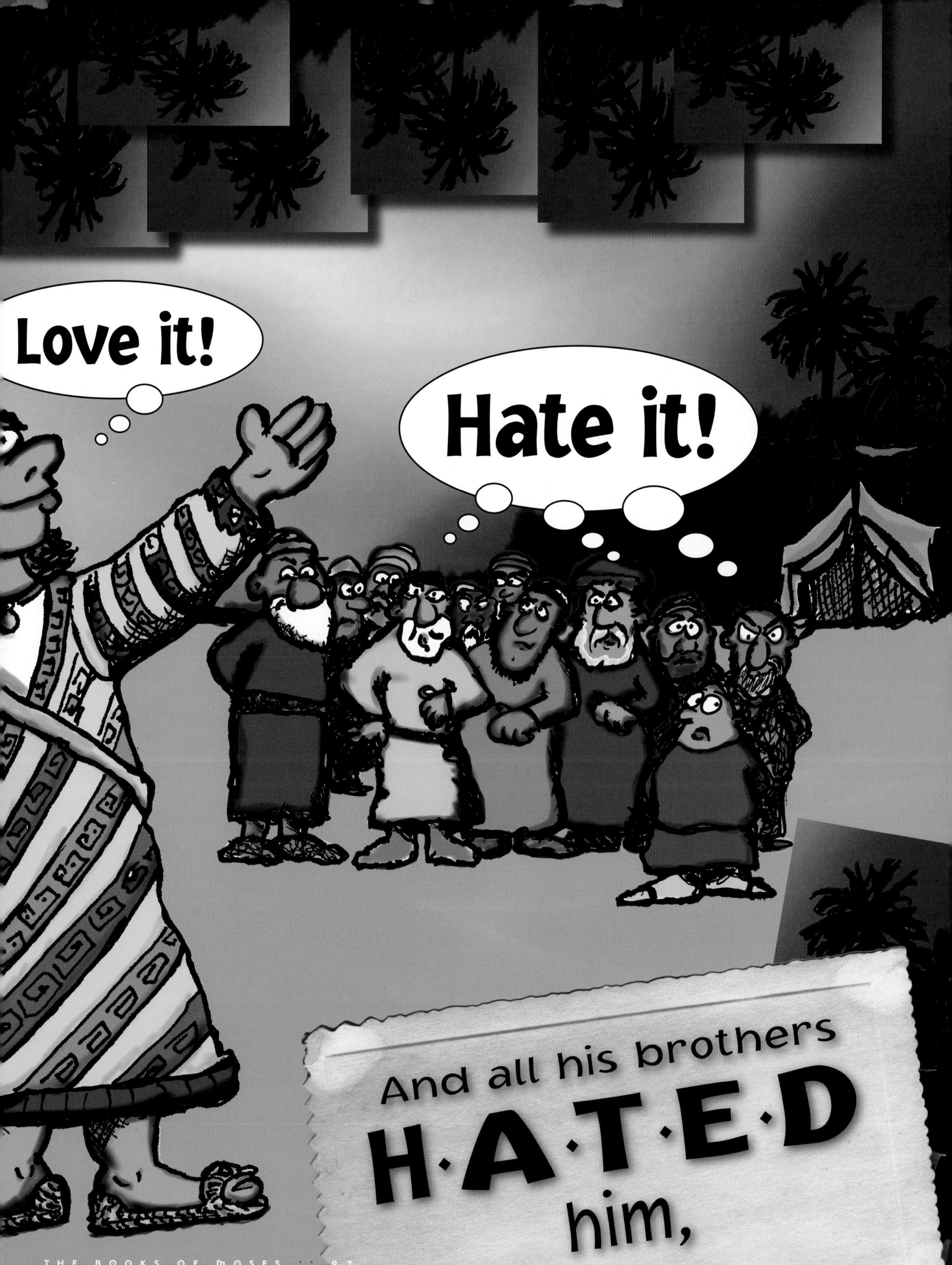
Love it!
Hate it!
And all his brothers
H·A·T·E·D
him,

They stripped him of his coat and threw him into a pit and sold him for **1 2 3 4 5 6 7 8 9 10 11 12 13 14 15 16 17 18 19 20** pieces of SILVER SILVER SILVER SILVER SILVER SIL

*Sheol - the place of the dead

They took Joseph's robe and dipped the robe in blood. Then Jacob tore his garments, and all his sons and all his daughters, they sought to comfort him.

Meanwhile, Joseph was taken as a slave to

Egypt.

SILVER.

Joseph went through many trials and adventures as a slave. He ran away from his master's wife when she tried to kiss him. He was caught and thrown in jail. There he interpreted dreams for all the prisoners.

Egypt could use a good man like you. Do you want the job? What do you say?

Many years later, Joseph's brothers traveled to Egypt looking for food. He fed them and finally told them who he was. He forgave them, then brought all of Israel's family to live with him in Egypt.

Forgive us!

One of the prisoners was Pharaoh's cup holder. When the man was released, he told the mighty ruler about Joseph. Pharaoh asked Joseph to interpret his dreams, too. Joseph did just that, and the next thing he knew, he was given the task of getting all of Egypt ready for a famine that was coming.

GSI (God Scene Investigation) Verse: Genesis 50:20

Find the hidden Bible verse in this cartoon and highlight it in your Bible. Then go to *www.faithink.com* and type in FINK*link* BM07 to learn it in song and sign language.

Put me in charge and you won't be sorry!

And Joseph said: "Even though you intended to do harm to me, God intended it for...

good!"

The Home Huddle Journal
JOURNAL

VERSE OF THE WEEK

But Joseph said, "Even though you intended to do harm to me, God intended it for good."

Genesis 50:20

Day 1

my **High** today was:

my **Low** today was:

my **Prayer** today is:

Day 2

my **High** today was:

my **Low** today was:

my **Prayer** today is:

Day 3

my **High** today was:

my **Low** today was:

my **Prayer** today is:

Learn sign language for this verse using FINKlink

BM07 | @ www.faithink.com

1. **Share** Highs & Lows of the day
2. **Read** sing, sign and highlight the verse of the week in your Bibles
3. **Talk** about how the verse relates to your Highs & Lows
4. **Pray** for your Highs & Lows, for your family and for the world
5. **Bless** one another using this week's blessing (bottom of next page)

Day 4

my **High** today was:

my **Low** today was:

my **Prayer** today is:

Day 5

my **High** today was:

my **Low** today was:

my **Prayer** today is:

Day 6

my **High** today was:

my **Low** today was:

my **Prayer** today is:

ART ATTACK

Create your own artwork to help tell this week's story:

R The Week in REVIEW

THIS WEEK'S BLESSING

(Name), child of God, may God turn your lows into highs before your very eyes!

Looking back on the week, my highest **High** was:

....

My lowest **Low** this week was:

....

One way God answered my **Prayers** this week was:

....

One way God might use me as a **Sacred Agent** to help answer another person's prayers:

....

....

FAMILY COVENANT

Our family has shared **Highs & Lows** this week, **read** the cartoon Bible story and high-lighted the theme verse in our Bibles, **talked** about our lives, **prayed** for one another's highs and lows, and **blessed** one another.

....
Parent's Signature   **Child's Signature**   **Date**

Son of His Old Age

by Rich Melheim   Online at www.faithink.com
Genesis 37:3, 4b, 23, 24a, 28b, 31, 34a, 35, 50:20

Now Israel loved Joseph
    because he was the son of his old age
More than any other of his children
    because he was the son of his old age
And he had made him a coat of many colors
    because he was the son of his old age
And all his brothers, they hated him
    because he was the son of his old age

And Joseph said, "Even though you intended
    to do harm to me"
And Joseph said, "Even though you intended harm
    God intended it for good"

All his brothers, they hated him
    because he was the son of his old age
They stripped him of his robe and threw him into a pit
    because he was the son of his old age
And sold him for 20 pieces of silver
    because he was the son of his old age
And they took Joseph to Egypt
    because he was the son of his old age

And Joseph said, "Even though you intended..."

They took Joseph's robe and dipped the robe in blood
    because he was the son of his old age
Then Jacob tore his garment
    because he was the son of his old age
And all his sons and all his daughters,
    they sought to comfort him
    because he was the son of his old age
"No, no, no, I shall go to Sheol to my son, mourning
    because he was the son of my old age"

And Joseph said, "Even though you intended..."

Because he was the son of my old age!

The Home Huddle Journal
JOURNAL

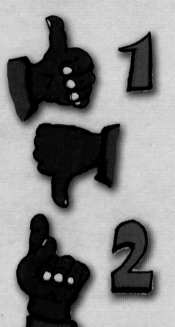

Day 1

my **High** today was:

my **Low** today was:

my **Prayer** today is:

Day 2

my **High** today was:

my **Low** today was:

my **Prayer** today is:

Day 3

my **High** today was:

my **Low** today was:

my **Prayer** today is:

1. **Share** Highs & Lows of the day
2. **Read** sing, sign and highlight the verse of the week in your Bibles
3. **Talk** about how the verse relates to your Highs & Lows
4. **Pray** for your Highs & Lows, for your family and for the world
5. **Bless** one another using this week's blessing (bottom of next page)

Day 4

my **High** today was:

my **Low** today was:

my **Prayer** today is:

Day 5

my **High** today was:

my **Low** today was:

my **Prayer** today is:

Day 6

my **High** today was:

my **Low** today was:

my **Prayer** today is:

VERSE OF THE WEEK

But Joseph said, "Even though you intended to do harm to me, God intended it for good."

Genesis 50:20

Learn sign language for this verse using FINKlink
BM07 | @ www.faithink.com

ART ATTACK

Create your own artwork to help tell this week's story:

The Week in REVIEW

THIS WEEK'S BLESSING

(Name), child of God, may God turn your lows into highs before your very eyes!

Looking back on the week, my highest **High** was:

....

My lowest **Low** this week was:

....

One way God answered my **Prayers** this week was:

....

One way God might use me as a **Sacred Agent** to help answer another person's prayers:

....

....

FAMILY COVENANT

Our family has shared **Highs & Lows** this week, **read** the cartoon Bible story and high-lighted the theme verse in our Bibles, **talked** about our lives, **prayed** for one another's highs and lows, and **blessed** one another.

....
Parent's Signature   **Child's Signature**   **Date**

Name that Verse

1. **Divide** into small groups or teams.
2. **Listen** to eight short Bible Song clips at www.faithink.com.
3. **Guess** the location of each verse. Write your answer below.
4. **Award** the following points for each correct answer:

> * **Old or New Testament**   5 points
> * **Correct Bible Book, Chapter & Verse**   10 points

5. **Record** your scores immediately in the boxes to the right.
6. **Add** subtotal of all correct answers in the box. (80 Possible)
7. **Play** Bonus Round. Get all correct and score 20 extra pts.
8. **Total** results and award prizes for added fun.

JOSEPH'S COAT BY HE QI
WWW.HEQIARTS.COM

Order this art print using FINKlink
BM07 | @ www.faithink.com

Answer Key

CHOOSE EIGHT FROM THE FOLLOWING VERSES

	Old or New Testament	Book, Chapter, Verse	
Song 1			☐
Song 2			☐
Song 3			☐
Song 4			☐
Song 5			☐
Song 6			☐
Song 7			☐
Song 8			☐
		Subtotal	☐

Genesis 1:1-3

Genesis 3:8-9

Genesis 15:5

Genesis 22:7-8

Genesis 28:11-13

Genesis 50:20

Exodus 3:1-8

Leviticus 6:24-26

Numbers 6:24-26

Psalm 23:1-6

Matthew 6:9-11

John 1:1-3

BONUS ROUND
(Add 20 points if perfect order)   ☐ ☐ ☐ ☐ ☐

Play this online game using FINKlink
BM07 | @ www.faithink.com

Final Score   ☐

FAITH INKUBATORS

Work or Die!

Joseph's Family

lived peacefully in Egypt for 400 years. They grew in numbers and prospered. Then a terrible thing happened. A new Pharaoh who did not remember Joseph arose. Threatened by Israel's power, he turned all of Israel into slaves and ordered their baby boys put to death!

Listen to this song using FINKlink
BM08 | @ www.faithink.com

What's this?

One frightened woman placed her baby into a basket and floated it down the river toward Pharaoh's daughter. The princess pulled it from the waters and named the baby Moses.*

You're pretty **smart!**

*Moses means "drawn out of the water"

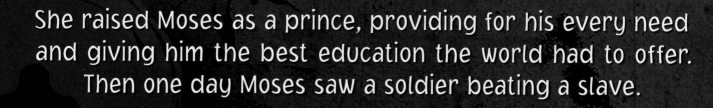

She raised Moses as a prince, providing for his every need and giving him the best education the world had to offer. Then one day Moses saw a soldier beating a slave.

He tried to stop the beating and hit the soldier. The soldier died. Moses was forced to run away into the desert **wilderness.**

GSI (God Scene Investigation) Verse: Exodus 3:1-2a, 4b-
Find the hidden Bible verse in this cartoon and highlight it in your Bible. Then go to
www.faithink.com and type in FINK*link* BM08 to learn it in song and sign language.

Moses was keeping the flock of his father-in-law Jethro, the priest of Midian; he led his flock beyond the wilderness, and came to Horeb, the mountain of God. There an angel of the Lord appeared to him in a flame of fire out of a bush.

God called, "Moses!" He said, "Here I am." "The place on which you are standing is holy ground. I am the God of your father, the God of Abraham, the God of Isaac, the God of Jacob, too. I have observed the misery of my people. I have heard their cry... Indeed, I know their sufferings, and I have come down to deliver them." But Moses said:

If I say to them, "The God of your ancestors has sent me to you," and they ask me, "What is his name?" What shall I say to them?

I AM WHO I AM

And Moses went down to **Egypt** and did as the Lord God commanded.

HERE'S A HIGH!

The Home Huddle Journal
JOURNAL

VERSE OF THE WEEK

Moses was keeping the flock of his father-in-law Jethro, the priest of Midian; he led his flock beyond the wilderness, and came to Horeb, the mountain of God. There the angel of the Lord appeared to him in a flame of fire out of a bush. God called, "Moses!" He said, "Here I am."

Exodus 3:1-2a, 4b

Day 1

my **High** today was:

my **Low** today was:

my **Prayer** today is:

Day 2

my **High** today was:

my **Low** today was:

my **Prayer** today is:

Day 3

my **High** today was:

my **Low** today was:

my **Prayer** today is:

Learn sign language for this verse using FINKlink

BM08 | @ www.faithink.com

1. **Share** Highs & Lows of the day
2. **Read** sing, sign and highlight the verse of the week in your Bibles
3. **Talk** about how the verse relates to your Highs & Lows
4. **Pray** for your Highs & Lows, for your family and for the world
5. **Bless** one another using this week's blessing (bottom of next page)

Day 4

my **High** today was:

my **Low** today was:

my **Prayer** today is:

Day 5

my **High** today was:

my **Low** today was:

my **Prayer** today is:

Day 6

my **High** today was:

my **Low** today was:

my **Prayer** today is:

 **ATTACK**

Create your own artwork to help tell this week's story:

 **The Week in REVIEW**

Looking back on the week, my highest **High** was:

....

My lowest **Low** this week was:

....

One way God answered my **Prayers** this week was:

....

One way God might use me as a **Sacred Agent** to help answer another person's prayers:

....

....

Family Covenant

Our family has shared **Highs & Lows** this week, **read** the cartoon Bible story and highlighted the theme verse in our Bibles, **talked** about our lives, **prayed** for one another's highs and lows, and **blessed** one another.

....

Parent's Signature   **Child's Signature**   **Date**

The Burning Bush

by Rich Melheim   Online at www.faithink.com
Exodus 3:1-2a, 4b , 5b-6a, 7-8a, 13-14a

Moses was keeping the flock of his
father-in-law Jethro, priest of Midian
He led his flock beyond the wilderness
and he came to Horeb, the mountain of God
There an angel of the Lord appeared to him
in a flame of fire out of a bush
God called, "Moses!" He said, "Here I am!"
"The place on which you are standing
is holy ground"

"I am the God of your father, the God of Abraham,
the God of Isaac, and of Jacob, too
I have heard their cry, I've come down to deliver them
I am who I am, I am who
I am who I am!"

"I have observed the misery of my people,
I have heard their cry
Indeed, I know their sufferings,
And I have come down, indeed, I"
But Moses said, "God, if I say to them
'The God of your ancestors has sent me to you,'
And they ask me, 'What is his name?'
What shall I say to them?"
"I am who I am, I am who..."

I am the God of your father...

Listen to this song using FINKlink
BM08 @ www.faithink.com

The Home Huddle Journal

JOURNAL

Week 2

Day 1

my **High** today was:

my **Low** today was:

my **Prayer** today is:

Day 2

my **High** today was:

my **Low** today was:

my **Prayer** today is:

Day 3

my **High** today was:

my **Low** today was:

my **Prayer** today is:

1. **Share** Highs & Lows of the day
2. **Read** sing, sign and highlight the verse of the week in your Bibles
3. **Talk** about how the verse relates to your Highs & Lows
4. **Pray** for your Highs & Lows, for your family and for the world
5. **Bless** one another using this week's blessing (bottom of next page)

Day 4

my **High** today was:

my **Low** today was:

my **Prayer** today is:

Day 5

my **High** today was:

my **Low** today was:

my **Prayer** today is:

Day 6

my **High** today was:

my **Low** today was:

my **Prayer** today is:

VERSE OF THE WEEK

Moses was keeping the flock of his father-in-law Jethro, the priest of Midian; he led his flock beyond the wilderness, and came to Horeb, the mountain of God. There the angel of the Lord appeared to him in a flame of fire out of a bush. God called, "Moses!" He said, "Here I am."

Exodus 3:1-2a, 4b

Learn sign language for this verse using FINKlink

BM08 | @ www.faithink.com

Art ATTACK

Create your own artwork to help tell this week's story:

The Week in REVIEW

THIS WEEK'S BLESSING

(Name), child
of God, may you
hear and obey
God's call
this day.

Looking back on the week, my highest **High** was:

My lowest **Low** this week was:

One way God answered my **Prayers** this week was:

One way God might use me as a **Sacred Agent** to help answer another person's prayers:

FAMILY COVENANT

Our family has shared **Highs & Lows** this week, **read** the cartoon Bible story and high-lighted the theme verse in our Bibles, **talked** about our lives, **prayed** for one another's highs and lows, and **blessed** one another.

Parent's Signature   Child's Signature   Date

Name That Verse

The Burning Bush by He Qi
www.heqiarts.com

Order this art print using FINKlink
BM08 @ www.faithink.com

1. **Divide** into small groups or teams.
2. **Listen** to eight short Bible Song clips at www.faithink.com.
3. **Guess** the location of each verse. Write your answer below.
4. **Award** the following points for each correct answer:

* **Old or New Testament**	5 points
* **Correct Bible Book, Chapter & Verse**	10 points

5. **Record** your scores immediately in the boxes to the right.
6. **Add** subtotal of all correct answers in the box. (80 Possible)
7. **Play** Bonus Round. Get all correct and score 20 extra pts.
8. **Total** results and award prizes for added fun.

Answer Key

Choose eight from the following verses

Old or New Testament   Book, Chapter, Verse

Song 1 _____

Song 2 _____

Song 3 _____

Song 4 _____

Song 5 _____

Song 6 _____

Song 7 _____

Song 8 _____

Subtotal

Bonus Round
(Add 20 points if perfect order)

Genesis 1:1-3

Genesis 9:13-14

Genesis 15:5

Genesis 22:7-8

Genesis 28:11-13

Genesis 50:20

Exodus 3:1-8

Exodus 12:3-7

Numbers 6:24-26

Leviticus 19:2

Exodus 20:2-3

Matthew 6:9-11

Play this online game using FINKlink
BM08 @ www.faithink.com

Final Score

FAITH INKUBATORS

PHARA

Moses

did as God commanded. He ordered the mighty ruler of Egypt to set his slaves free, but the king did not obey. So God sent 10 terrible plagues against Egypt. First, the rivers turned blood red! But Pharaoh would not let Israel go free.

Listen to this song using FINKlink
BM09 @ www.faithink.com

Aaaaaaah!

moooooooooooooh!*

reeeeedeeep!**

GSI (God Scene Investigation) Verse: Exodus 12:3a

Find the hidden Bible verse in this cartoon and highlight it in your Bible. Then go to *www.faithink.com* and type in FINK*link* BM09 to learn it in song and sign language.

* "Moooo!" is Cow for "Aaaaaaah!"   **"Reeedeep!" is Frog for "Reeedeep!"

"For I will pass through the land...

Next, frogs covered the land. Then biting gnats appeared. Then flies, but still Pharaoh did not let Israel go. Next a plague killed the animals. Then people were infected with oozing sores. Then hail and fire fell from heaven. Then grasshoppers. Then darkness covered the land. Finally God told Moses: "Tell the whole congregation of Israel they are to take a lamb. Your lamb shall be without blemish..."

"You shall slaughter it at twilight. Take some blood and put it on the two door posts and the lintels of the houses..."

I will strike down every firstborn."

"The blood shall be a sign for you on the houses where you live. When I see the blood I will **PASS OVER** you and no plague shall destroy you." Thus says the Lord: "About midnight I will go out... every first-born in the land shall die. There will be a loud cry such as has never been nor will ever be again."

That night, just as God said, the Angel of Death **PASSED OVER** the land of Egypt and killed all the firstborn sons of the land... from the poorest of the slaves to the mighty Pharaoh's own house. And that night God's people won their freedom.

The Home Huddle Journal
journal

VERSE OF THE WEEK

Tell the whole congregation of Israel... they are to take a lamb...

Exodus 12:3a

Day 1

my **High** today was:

my **Low** today was:

my **Prayer** today is:

Day 2

my **High** today was:

my **Low** today was:

my **Prayer** today is:

Day 3

my **High** today was:

my **Low** today was:

my **Prayer** today is:

1. **Share** Highs & Lows of the day
2. **Read** sing, sign and highlight the verse of the week in your Bibles
3. **Talk** about how the verse relates to your Highs & Lows
4. **Pray** for your Highs & Lows, for your family and for the world
5. **Bless** one another using this week's blessing (bottom of next page)

Day 4

my **High** today was:

my **Low** today was:

my **Prayer** today is:

Day 5

my **High** today was:

my **Low** today was:

my **Prayer** today is:

Day 6

my **High** today was:

my **Low** today was:

my **Prayer** today is:

ART ATTACK

Create your own artwork to help tell this week's story:

The Week in REVIEW

THIS WEEK'S BLESSING

(name), child of God, may God's holy angels pass over you and protect you this day.

Looking back on the week, my highest **High** was:

....

My lowest **Low** this week was:

....

One way God answered my **Prayers** this week was:

....

One way God might use me as a **Sacred Agent** to help answer another person's prayers:

....

....

FAMILY COVENANT

Our family has shared **Highs & Lows** this week, **read** the cartoon Bible story and highlighted the theme verse in our Bibles, **talked** about our lives, **prayed** for one another's highs and lows, and **blessed** one another.

....
Parent's Signature   **Child's Signature**   **Date**

Take a Lamb

by Rich Melheim   Online at www.faithink.com
Exodus 11:5a; 12:3a, 5a, 6b-7, 12a, 13

Tell the whole congregation of Israel
they are to take a lamb (repeat)

Your lamb shall be without blemish
You shall slaughter it at twilight
Take some blood and put it on the two doorposts
and the lintel of the houses

For I will pass through the land
I will strike down every firstborn
The blood shall be a sign for you
On the houses where you live
When I see the blood, I will pass over you
and no plague shall destroy you

Thus says the Lord:
About midnight I will go out
Every firstborn in the land shall die
There will be a loud cry
such as has never been
or will ever be again

Tell the whole congregation of Israel
they are to take a lamb (repeat)

The Home Huddle Journal
JOURNAL

Week 2 (Use this if you're doing a theme every 2 weeks)

Day 1

my **High** today was:

my **Low** today was:

my **Prayer** today is:

Day 2

my **High** today was:

my **Low** today was:

my **Prayer** today is:

Day 3

my **High** today was:

my **Low** today was:

my **Prayer** today is:

1. **Share** Highs & Lows of the day
2. **Read** sing, sign and highlight the verse of the week in your Bibles
3. **Talk** about how the verse relates to your Highs & Lows
4. **Pray** for your Highs & Lows, for your family and for the world
5. **Bless** one another using this week's blessing (bottom of next page)

Day 4

my **High** today was:

my **Low** today was:

my **Prayer** today is:

VERSE OF THE WEEK

Tell the whole congregation of Israel... they are to take a lamb...

Exodus 12:3a

Day 5

my **High** today was:

my **Low** today was:

my **Prayer** today is:

Day 6

my **High** today was:

my **Low** today was:

my **Prayer** today is:

Learn sign language for this verse using FINKlink

BM09 | @ www.faithink.com

ART
ATTACK

Create your own artwork to help tell this week's story:

The Week in REVIEW

THIS WEEK'S BLESSING

(Name), child of God, may God's holy angels pass over you and protect you this day.

Looking back on the week, my highest **High** was:

....

My lowest **Low** this week was:

....

One way God answered my **Prayers** this week was:

....

One way God might use me as a **Sacred Agent** to help answer another person's prayers:

....

....

FAMILY COVENANT

Our family has shared **Highs & Lows** this week, **read** the cartoon Bible story and highlighted the theme verse in our Bibles, **talked** about our lives, **prayed** for one another's highs and lows, and **blessed** one another.

....

Parent's Signature   **Child's Signature**   **Date**

Name That Verse

1. **Divide** into small groups or teams.
2. **Listen** to eight short Bible Song clips at www.faithink.com.
3. **Guess** the location of each verse. Write your answer below.
4. **Award** the following points for each correct answer:

     * **Old or New Testament**   5 points
     * **Correct Bible Book, Chapter & Verse**   10 points

5. **Record** your scores immediately in the boxes to the right.
6. **Add** subtotal of all correct answers in the box. (80 Possible)
7. **Play** Bonus Round. Get all correct and score 20 extra pts.
8. **Total** results and award prizes for added fun.

Order this art print using FINKlink
BM09 @ www.faithink.com

GIDEON & THE ANGEL BY HE QI
www.HEQIARTS.com

	Old or New Testament	Book, Chapter, Verse	
Song 1			☐
Song 2			☐
Song 3			☐
Song 4			☐
Song 5			☐
Song 6			☐
Song 7			☐
Song 8			☐
		Subtotal	☐

Answer Key

Choose eight from the following verses

Genesis 1:1-3

Genesis 9:13-14

Genesis 15:5

Genesis 22:7-8

Genesis 50:20

Exodus 3:1-8

Exodus 12:3-7

Exodus 15:1

Numbers 6:24-26

Psalm 23:1-6

Isaiah 55:10-11

Amos 8:4-6

Bonus Round
(Add 20 points if perfect order)   ☐ ☐ ☐ ☐ ☐

Play this online game using FINKlink
BM09 @ www.faithink.com

Final Score   ☐

FAITH
INKUBATORS

I Will Sing to the Lord

Get out!

Mighty, Mighty Pharaoh

had seen enough! He called for Moses and his brother, Aaron, and told them to take their people, their plagues, and their God and get out of Egypt.

Listen to this song using FINKlink
BM10 @ www.faithink.com

Meanwhile back in Egypt, Pharaoh was having some second thoughts. The mighty king's heart hardened again. He called on his 600 crack charioteers to find the slaves and teach them a harsh lesson. A very harsh lesson.

Israel was camped by the sea when the chariots suddenly appeared on the horizon. They were trapped! The people cried out to Moses: "Why did you bring us out into the wilderness to die? We were better off in Egypt!" Then Moses prayed to the Lord God. God commanded Moses to stretch out his hand over the sea.

GSI (God Scene Investigation) Verse: Exodus 15:1-2

Find the hidden Bible verse in this cartoon and highlight it in your Bible. Then go to *www.faithink.com* and type in FINK*link* BM10 to learn it in song and sign language.

The waters parted! Israel scrambled quickly to safety on the other side. When Pharaoh's army tried to follow, their chariots got stuck and the waters covered them up! Then Moses and all Israel sang this song of praise: "I will sing to the Lord, for he has triumphed gloriously; horse and rider he has thrown into the sea."

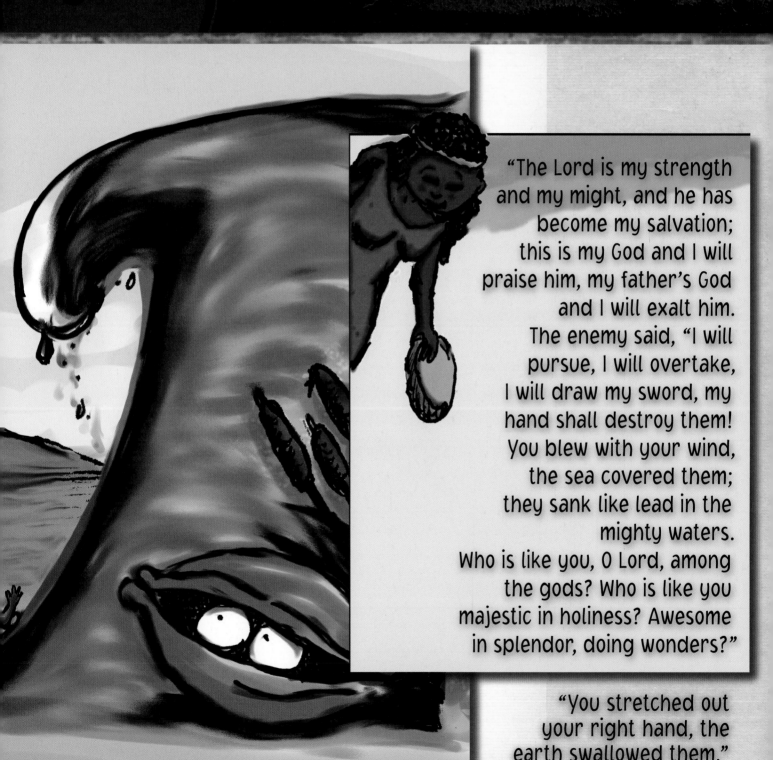

"The Lord is my strength and my might, and he has become my salvation; this is my God and I will praise him, my father's God and I will exalt him. The enemy said, "I will pursue, I will overtake, I will draw my sword, my hand shall destroy them! You blew with your wind, the sea covered them; they sank like lead in the mighty waters.
Who is like you, O Lord, among the gods? Who is like you majestic in holiness? Awesome in splendor, doing wonders?"

"You stretched out your right hand, the earth swallowed them."

Pharaoh, Pharaoh, oh baby, what's your high and low?

VERSE OF THE WEEK

I will sing to the Lord, for he has triumphed gloriously; horse and rider he has thrown into the sea. The Lord is my strength and my might, and he has become my salvation; this is my God, and I will praise him, my father's God, and I will exalt him.

Exodus 15:1-2

Day 1

my **High** today was:

my **Low** today was:

my **Prayer** today is:

Day 2

my **High** today was:

my **Low** today was:

my **Prayer** today is:

Day 3

my **High** today was:

my **Low** today was:

my **Prayer** today is:

Learn sign language for this verse using FINKlink

BM10 @ www.faithink.com

1. **Share** Highs & Lows of the day
2. **Read** sing, sign and highlight the verse of the week in your Bibles
3. **Talk** about how the verse relates to your Highs & Lows
4. **Pray** for your Highs & Lows, for your family and for the world
5. **Bless** one another using this week's blessing (bottom of next page)

Day 4

my **High** today was:

my **Low** today was:

my **Prayer** today is:

Day 5

my **High** today was:

my **Low** today was:

my **Prayer** today is:

Day 6

my **High** today was:

my **Low** today was:

my **Prayer** today is:

ATTACK

Create your own artwork to help tell this week's story:

The Week in REVIEW

This Week's Blessing

(Name), child of God, may God rescue you from every danger.

Looking back on the week, my highest **High** was:

My lowest **Low** this week was:

One way God answered my **Prayers** this week was:

One way God might use me as a **Sacred Agent** to help answer another person's prayers:

Family Covenant

Our family has shared **Highs & Lows** this week, **read** the cartoon Bible story and highlighted the theme verse in our Bibles, **talked** about our lives, **prayed** for one another's highs and lows, and **blessed** one another.

Parent's Signature   Child's Signature   Date

I Will Sing to the Lord
(Into the Sea)

by Rich Melheim & Todd Ernster   Online at www.faithink.com
Exodus 15:1-2, 9-12

I will sing to the Lord
    for he has triumphed gloriously;
    horse and rider he has thrown
    into the sea
I will sing to the Lord
    for he has triumphed gloriously
    horse and rider thrown
    into the sea

The Lord is my strength and my might
  and he has become my salvation
This is my God, and I will praise him
  My father's God, and I will exalt him

I will sing to the Lord...

The enemy said, "I will pursue, I will overtake,
  I will draw my sword, my hand shall destroy them"
You blew with your wind, the sea covered them
  They sank like lead in the mighty waters

I will sing to the Lord...

Who is like you, O Lord, among the gods?
  Who is like you, majestic in holiness,
  awesome in splendor, doing wonders one after another?
You stretched out your right hand,
  the earth swallowed them

I will sing to the Lord...

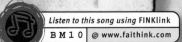

The Home Huddle Journal
JOURNAL

Day 1

my **High** today was:

my **Low** today was:

my **Prayer** today is:

Day 2

my **High** today was:

my **Low** today was:

my **Prayer** today is:

Day 3

my **High** today was:

my **Low** today was:

my **Prayer** today is:

1. **Share** Highs & Lows of the day
2. **Read** sing, sign and highlight the verse of the week in your Bibles
3. **Talk** about how the verse relates to your Highs & Lows
4. **Pray** for your Highs & Lows, for your family and for the world
5. **Bless** one another using this week's blessing (bottom of next page)

Day 4

my **High** today was:

my **Low** today was:

my **Prayer** today is:

Day 5

my **High** today was:

my **Low** today was:

my **Prayer** today is:

Day 6

my **High** today was:

my **Low** today was:

my **Prayer** today is:

VERSE OF THE WEEK

I will sing to the Lord, for he has triumphed gloriously; horse and rider he has thrown into the sea. The Lord is my strength and my might, and he has become my salvation; this is my God, and I will praise him, my father's God, and I will exalt him.

Exodus 15:1-2

Learn sign language for this verse using FINKlink
BM10 @ www.faithink.com

Art

Create your own artwork to help tell this week's story:

R The Week in Review

This Week's Blessing

(Name), child of God, may God rescue you from every danger.

Looking back on the week, my highest **High** was:

....

My lowest **Low** this week was:

....

One way God answered my **Prayers** this week was:

....

One way God might use me as a **Sacred Agent** to help answer another person's prayers:

....

....

Family Covenant

Our family has shared **Highs & Lows** this week, **read** the cartoon Bible story and highlighted the theme verse in our Bibles, **talked** about our lives, **prayed** for one another's highs and lows, and **blessed** one another.

....
Parent's Signature   **Child's Signature**   **Date**

Name That Verse

1. **Divide** into small groups or teams.
2. **Listen** to eight short Bible Song clips at www.faithink.com.
3. **Guess** the location of each verse. Write your answer below.
4. **Award** the following points for each correct answer:

   * **Old or New Testament**   5 points
   * **Correct Bible Book, Chapter & Verse**   10 points

5. **Record** your scores immediately in the boxes to the right.
6. **Add** subtotal of all correct answers in the box. (80 Possible)
7. **Play** Bonus Round. Get all correct and score 20 extra pts.
8. **Total** results and award prizes for added fun.

Order this art print using FINKlink
BM10 @ www.faithink.com

Red Sea Crossing by He Qi · www.HeQiArts.com

	Old or New Testament	Book, Chapter, Verse	
Song 1			☐
Song 2			☐
Song 3			☐
Song 4			☐
Song 5			☐
Song 6			☐
Song 7			☐
Song 8			☐
		Subtotal	☐

Answer Key

Choose eight from the following verses

Genesis 1:1-3

Genesis 9:13-14

Genesis 15:5

Genesis 28:11-13

Exodus 3:1-8

Exodus 12:3-7

Exodus 15:1

Exodus 20:2-3

Deuteronomy 6:6-9

Psalm 103:1-5

I David 17:45

I Samuel 17:45

Bonus Round
(Add 20 points if perfect order)
☐ ☐ ☐ ☐ ☐

Play this online game using FINKlink
BM10 @ www.faithink.com

Final Score ☐

FAITH INKUBATORS

Moses struck a rock and water gushed out.

Complain

Complain
Complain!

CO

Ever since their escape from Egypt,
the people of Israel did nothing but...

Moses! We don't have any **food!**

We're all gonna die!

We were better off in **Egypt!**

Manna?*

*Manna: Literally "what is it?"

The next morning God sent manna - bread from heaven.

That evening a flock of quail landed in the camp.

...MPLAIN!

RUMBLE RUMBLE

I AM
THE LORD YOUR GOD

You shall have
no other gods
before me.

You shall not make
for yourself an...

Honor you
father and
mother.

THE TEN
COMMA

On the third month after their daring escape from slavery, while camping at the base of Mount Sinai in the wilderness, the whole earth began to **quake**. The mountain was wrapped in **smoke** and **fire**. **Lightning** flashed and the people of Israel **trembled** in fear. Moses climbed to the top of the mountain, and there God gave him the laws that were to govern God's people. Maybe you've heard of them?

idol.

You shall not take the name of the Lord your God in **vain.**

Remember the **Sabbath day** and keep it **holy.**

You shall not **murder.**

You shall not commit **adultery.**

IDMENTS

You shall not bear **false witness** against your neighbor.

You shall not **covet** your neighbor's house;

You shall not **covet** your neighbor's wife, or male or female slave, or ox, or donkey, or anything that belongs to your neighbor.

All the words the Lord has spoken

WE WILL DO!

GSI (God Scene Investigation) Verse: Exodus 20:2-3

Find the hidden Bible verse in this cartoon and highlight it in your Bible. Then go to *www.faithink.com* and type in FINK*link* BM11 to learn it in song and sign language.

The Home Huddle Journal
JOURNAL

Week 1

VERSE OF THE WEEK

I am the Lord your God, who brought you out of the land of Egypt, out of the house of slavery; you shall have no other gods before me.

Exodus 20:2-3

Day 1

my **High** today was:

my **Low** today was:

my **Prayer** today is:

Day 2

my **High** today was:

my **Low** today was:

my **Prayer** today is:

Day 3

my **High** today was:

my **Low** today was:

my **Prayer** today is:

Learn sign language for this verse using FINKlink

BM11 | @ www.faithink.com

1. **Share** Highs & Lows of the day
2. **Read** sing, sign and highlight the verse of the week in your Bibles
3. **Talk** about how the verse relates to your Highs & Lows
4. **Pray** for your Highs & Lows, for your family and for the world
5. **Bless** one another using this week's blessing (bottom of next page)

Day 4

my **High** today was:

my **Low** today was:

my **Prayer** today is:

Day 5

my **High** today was:

my **Low** today was:

my **Prayer** today is:

Day 6

my **High** today was:

my **Low** today was:

my **Prayer** today is:

ARt
ATTACK

Create your own artwork to help tell this week's story:

The Week in REVIEW

THIS WEEK'S BLESSING

(name), child of God, may you love and trust God above everything else.

Looking back on the week, my highest **High** was:

....

My lowest **Low** this week was:

....

One way God answered my **Prayers** this week was:

....

One way God might use me as a **Sacred Agent** to help answer another person's prayers:

....

....

FAMILY COVENANT

Our family has shared **Highs & Lows** this week, **read** the cartoon Bible story and high-lighted the theme verse in our Bibles, **talked** about our lives, **prayed** for one another's highs and lows, and **blessed** one another.

....

Parent's Signature   **Child's Signature**   **Date**

I Am!

by Todd Ernster   Online at www.faithink.com
Exodus 20:2-3 (with explanation by Dr. Martin Luther)

I am the Lord your God
who brought you out
of the land of Egypt
I am the Lord your God
who brought you out of
the house of slavery
I am the Lord your God,
you shall have no other gods before me
I am the Lord your God
who brought you out
of the land of Egypt

I am who I am, who I am
I am who I am, who I am
I am

The First Commandment:
"You shall have no other gods"
We are to fear, love,
and trust God above anything else
(repeat)

Listen to this song using FINKlink
B M 1 1 @ www.faithink.com

The Home Huddle Journal

JOURNAL

Week 2 (Use this if you're doing a theme every 2 weeks)

Day 1

my **High** today was:

my **Low** today was:

my **Prayer** today is:

Day 2

my **High** today was:

my **Low** today was:

my **Prayer** today is:

Day 3

my **High** today was:

my **Low** today was:

my **Prayer** today is:

1. **Share** Highs & Lows of the day
2. **Read** sing, sign and highlight the verse of the week in your Bibles
3. **Talk** about how the verse relates to your Highs & Lows
4. **Pray** for your Highs & Lows, for your family and for the world
5. **Bless** one another using this week's blessing (bottom of next page)

Day 4

my **High** today was:

my **Low** today was:

my **Prayer** today is:

Day 5

my **High** today was:

my **Low** today was:

my **Prayer** today is:

Day 6

my **High** today was:

my **Low** today was:

my **Prayer** today is:

VERSE OF THE WEEK

I am the Lord your God, who brought you out of the land of Egypt, out of the house of slavery; you shall have no other gods before me.

Exodus 20:2-3

Learn sign language for this verse using FINKlink
BM11 @ www.faithink.com

ART ATTACK

Create your own artwork to help tell this week's story:

The Week in REVIEW

THIS WEEK'S BLESSING

(Name), child of God, may you love and trust God above everything else.

Looking back on the week, my highest **High** was:

....

My lowest **Low** this week was:

....

One way God answered my **Prayers** this week was:

....

One way God might use me as a **Sacred Agent** to help answer another person's prayers:

....

....

FAMILY COVENANT

Our family has shared **Highs & Lows** this week, **read** the cartoon Bible story and highlighted the theme verse in our Bibles, **talked** about our lives, **prayed** for one another's highs and lows, and **blessed** one another.

....
Parent's Signature **Child's Signature** **Date**

Name That Verse

1. **Divide** into small groups or teams.
2. **Listen** to eight short Bible Song clips at www.faithink.com.
3. **Guess** the location of each verse. Write your answer below.
4. **Award** the following points for each correct answer:

   * **Old or New Testament**   5 points
   * **Correct Bible Book, Chapter & Verse**   10 points

5. **Record** your scores immediately in the boxes to the right.
6. **Add** subtotal of all correct answers in the box. (80 Possible)
7. **Play** Bonus Round. Get all correct and score 20 extra pts.
8. **Total** results and award prizes for added fun.

MOSES STRIKING ROCK BY HE QI · WWW.HEQIARTS.COM

BM11 | @ www.faithink.com

Answer Key
Choose eight from the following verses

Genesis 1:1-3

Genesis 9:13-14

Genesis 15:5

Exodus 1:1-3

Exodus 12:3-7

Exodus 15:1

Exodus 20:2-3

Numbers 23:19

Deuteronomy 6:6-9

Nahum 1:7-8

John 1:1-3

Revelation 3:20

	Old or New Testament	Book, Chapter, Verse	
Song 1			☐
Song 2			☐
Song 3			☐
Song 4			☐
Song 5			☐
Song 6			☐
Song 7			☐
Song 8			☐
		Subtotal	☐

Bonus Round ☐ ☐ ☐ ☐ ☐
(Add 20 points if perfect order)

Play this online game using FINKlink
BM11 | @ www.faithink.com

Final Score ☐

FAITH INKUBATORS

What's taking them so long?

Traffic?

The Lord

told Moses to wait on Mount Sinai and he would be given two stone tablets containing God's Ten Commandments. Moses took his assistant, Joshua, and climbed to the top. Forty days and forty nights came and went. The people grew impatient.

Listen to this song using FINKlink
BM12 @ www.faithink.com

As Moses walked down the mountain, he heard what sounded like a great battle going on in the camp below. But it wasn't a battle, it was a drunken party! The people were dancing around the golden calf and shouting praises. Moses was so angry that he hurled the two stone commandment tablets at them, smashing them to pieces!

All the sons of Levi gathered around him. They strapped swords on their sides and went through the camp...

Who is on the **Lord's** side?

...killing every idol worshipper.*

*Do not try this at home. Instead, ask, "What would Rabbi Jesus do?"

On that day the

LEV

Moses pounded the calf into powder and mixed it with water. He made the unfaithful people drink the bitter water. Some Israelites were sorry. Others were not. Moses was miffed. He stood at the gate of the camp.

ITES

became the priests of Israel.

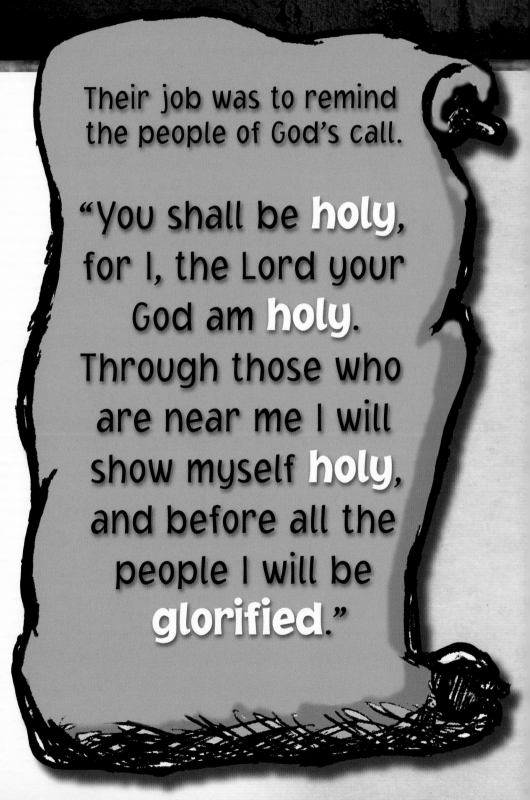

Their job was to remind the people of God's call.

"You shall be **holy**, for I, the Lord your God am **holy**. Through those who are near me I will show myself **holy**, and before all the people I will be **glorified**."

The Home Huddle Journal

JOURNAL

VERSE OF THE WEEK

Through those who are near me I will show myself holy, and before all the people I will be glorified.

You shall be holy, for I the Lord your God am holy.

Leviticus 10:3, 19:2

Day 1

my **High** today was:

my **Low** today was:

my **Prayer** today is:

Day 2

my **High** today was:

my **Low** today was:

my **Prayer** today is:

Day 3

my **High** today was:

my **Low** today was:

my **Prayer** today is:

Learn sign language for this verse using FINKlink
BM12 | @ www.faithink.com

1. **Share** Highs & Lows of the day
2. **Read** sing, sign and highlight the verse of the week in your Bibles
3. **Talk** about how the verse relates to your Highs & Lows
4. **Pray** for your Highs & Lows, for your family and for the world
5. **Bless** one another using this week's blessing (bottom of next page)

Day 4

my **High** today was:

my **Low** today was:

my **Prayer** today is:

Day 5

my **High** today was:

my **Low** today was:

my **Prayer** today is:

Day 6

my **High** today was:

my **Low** today was:

my **Prayer** today is:

 **ATTACK**

Create your own artwork to help tell this week's story:

 **The Week in REVIEW**

Looking back on the week, my highest **High** was:

....

My lowest **Low** this week was:

....

One way God answered my **Prayers** this week was:

....

One way God might use me as a **Sacred Agent** to help answer another person's prayers:

....

....

FAMILY COVENANT

Our family has shared **Highs & Lows** this week, **read** the cartoon Bible story and high-lighted the theme verse in our Bibles, **talked** about our lives, **prayed** for one another's highs and lows, and **blessed** one another.

....
Parent's Signature   **Child's Signature**   **Date**

You Shall Be Holy

by Rich Melheim   Online at www.faithink.com
Leviticus 10:3, 19:2

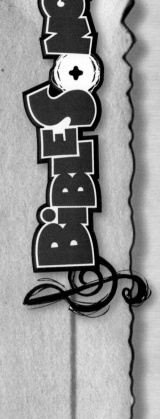

You shall be holy
You shall be holy
for I the Lord your God am holy
(repeat)

Through those who are near me
I will show myself holy
and before all the people
I will be glorified

You shall be holy
You shall be holy
for I the Lord your God am holy
(repeat)

For I the Lord your God am holy

Listen to this song using FINKlink
B M 1 2 @ www.faithink.com

The Home Huddle Journal
JOURNAL

Week 2 (Use this if you're doing a theme every 2 weeks)

1

2

3

4

5

Day 1

my **High** today was:

my **Low** today was:

my **Prayer** today is:

Day 2

my **High** today was:

my **Low** today was:

my **Prayer** today is:

Day 3

my **High** today was:

my **Low** today was:

my **Prayer** today is:

1. **Share** Highs & Lows of the day
2. **Read** sing, sign and highlight the verse of the week in your Bibles
3. **Talk** about how the verse relates to your Highs & Lows
4. **Pray** for your Highs & Lows, for your family and for the world
5. **Bless** one another using this week's blessing (bottom of next page)

Day 4

my **High** today was:

my **Low** today was:

my **Prayer** today is:

Day 5

my **High** today was:

my **Low** today was:

my **Prayer** today is:

Day 6

my **High** today was:

my **Low** today was:

my **Prayer** today is:

VERSE OF THE WEEK

Through those who are near me I will show myself holy, and before all the people I will be glorified.

You shall be holy, for I the Lord your God am holy.

Leviticus 10:3, 19:2

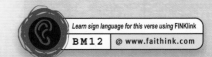

Learn sign language for this verse using FINKlink

BM12 @ www.faithink.com

ART ATTACK

Create your own artwork to help tell this week's story:

The Week in REVIEW

THIS WEEK'S BLESSING

(Name), child of God, may you be clean and right and true in all you say and do.

Looking back on the week, my highest **High** was:

....

My lowest **Low** this week was:

....

One way God answered my **Prayers** this week was:

....

One way God might use me as a **Sacred Agent** to help answer another person's prayers:

....

....

FAMILY COVENANT

Our family has shared **Highs & Lows** this week, **read** the cartoon Bible story and highlighted the theme verse in our Bibles, **talked** about our lives, **prayed** for one another's highs and lows, and **blessed** one another.

....

Parent's Signature   **Child's Signature**   **Date**

Name That Verse

1. **Divide** into small groups or teams.
2. **Listen** to eight short Bible Song clips at www.faithink.com.
3. **Guess** the location of each verse. Write your answer below.
4. **Award** the following points for each correct answer:

   * **Old or New Testament** — 5 points
   * **Correct Bible Book, Chapter & Verse** — 10 points

5. **Record** your scores immediately in the boxes to the right.
6. **Add** subtotal of all correct answers in the box. (80 Possible)
7. **Play** Bonus Round. Get all correct and score 20 extra pts.
8. **Total** results and award prizes for added fun.

Order this art print using FINKlink
BM12 @ www.faithink.com

THE TEN COMMANDMENTS BY HE QI
WWW.HEQIARTS.COM

Answer Key
Choose eight from the following verses

	Old or New Testament	Book, Chapter, Verse	
Song 1			☐
Song 2			☐
Song 3			☐
Song 4			☐
Song 5			☐
Song 6			☐
Song 7			☐
Song 8			☐
		Subtotal	☐

Genesis 1:1-3

Genesis 22:7-8

Exodus 15:1

Exodus 20:2-3

Leviticus 19:2

Numbers 6:24-26

Numbers 23:19

Jonah 2:1-2

Haggai 2:4-5

Matthew 15:13-16

Mark 15:13-16

Acts 15:13-16

Bonus Round
(Add 20 points if perfect order)   ☐ ☐ ☐ ☐ ☐

Play this online game using FINKlink
BM12 @ www.faithink.com

Final Score   ☐

FAITH INKUBATORS

It was time to take a census. Two years after their daring escape from Egypt, God told Moses to gather all the people to count the **numbers** of each of the twelve tribes of Israel.

Listen to this song using FINKlink
BM13 | @ www.faithink.com

In those days, Moses used to pitch a tent outside the camp where he would go to talk to God. Whenever he entered this "Tent of Meeting" a cloud would descend on it. After his conversation prayer with God, he would go out and teach the people everything God had told him. In this way the Lord trained the children of Israel in right and holy living.

GSI (God Scene Investigation) Verse: Numbers 6:24-26
Find the hidden Bible verse in this cartoon and highlight it in your Bible. Then go to *www.faithink.com* and type in FINK*link* BM13 to learn it in song and sign language.

He's rather **intense.**

God made a second set of stone tablets with the 10 commandments written on them to replace the ones Moses smashed. Moses then invited the very best artists in Israel to create a huge, beautiful tent and a great golden box to hold all of the holy things.

ARF!*

* Dog for: "You got that right!"

Moses called the tent a "Tabernacle" and the box was called the "Ark of the Covenant." Wherever they went, the soldiers of Israel always carried the ark ahead of them.

As they traveled, a cloud would lead them by day and a pillar of fire would lead them by night.

This reminded Israel that God was their protector, defender, and guide. In this way the Lord blessed and led Israel on the way to the **Promised Land.** One day God gave Aaron a very special blessing to share with the people:

"The Lord bless you and keep you; the Lord make his face to shine upon you, and be gracious to you; the Lord lift up his countenance upon you, and give you peace."

These words are called **Aaron's Blessing** to this very day.

VERSE OF THE WEEK

The Lord bless you and keep you; the Lord make his face to shine upon you, and be gracious to you; the Lord lift up his countenance upon you, and give you peace.

Numbers 6:24-26

Day 1

my **High** today was:

my **Low** today was:

my **Prayer** today is:

Day 2

my **High** today was:

my **Low** today was:

my **Prayer** today is:

Day 3

my **High** today was:

my **Low** today was:

my **Prayer** today is:

Learn sign language for this verse using FINKlink
BM13 | @ www.faithink.com

1. **Share** Highs & Lows of the day
2. **Read** sing, sign and highlight the verse of the week in your Bibles
3. **Talk** about how the verse relates to your Highs & Lows
4. **Pray** for your Highs & Lows, for your family and for the world
5. **Bless** one another using this week's blessing (bottom of next page)

Day 4

my **High** today was:

my **Low** today was:

my **Prayer** today is:

Day 5

my **High** today was:

my **Low** today was:

my **Prayer** today is:

Day 6

my **High** today was:

my **Low** today was:

my **Prayer** today is:

Art ATTACK

Create your own artwork to help tell this week's story:

The Week in REVIEW

THIS WEEK'S BLESSING

(Name), child of God, may God bless you and keep you. May God's face shine upon you. May God be gracious to you and give you peace.

Looking back on the week, my highest **High** was:

....

My lowest **Low** this week was:

....

One way God answered my **Prayers** this week was:

....

One way God might use me as a **Sacred Agent** to help answer another person's prayers:

....

....

FAMILY COVENANT

Our family has shared **Highs & Lows** this week, **read** the cartoon Bible story and high-lighted the theme verse in our Bibles, **talked** about our lives, **prayed** for one another's highs and lows, and **blessed** one another.

....
Parent's Signature   **Child's Signature**   **Date**

The Lord Bless You & Keep You

by Jon Anderson **Online at www.faithink.com**
Numbers 6:24-26

The Lord bless you
and keep you
The Lord make his face to
shine upon you and be
gracious to you
The Lord lift up his
countenance upon you
and give you peace
and give you peace

Listen to this song using FINKlink
BM13 @ www.faithink.com

The Home Huddle Journal
jOURNAL

Week 2 (use this if you're doing a theme every 2 weeks)

Day 1

my **High** today was:

my **Low** today was:

my **Prayer** today is:

Day 2

my **High** today was:

my **Low** today was:

my **Prayer** today is:

Day 3

my **High** today was:

my **Low** today was:

my **Prayer** today is:

1. **Share** Highs & Lows of the day
2. **Read** sing, sign and highlight the verse of the week in your Bibles
3. **Talk** about how the verse relates to your Highs & Lows
4. **Pray** for your Highs & Lows, for your family and for the world
5. **Bless** one another using this week's blessing (bottom of next page)

Day 4

my **High** today was:

my **Low** today was:

my **Prayer** today is:

Day 5

my **High** today was:

my **Low** today was:

my **Prayer** today is:

Day 6

my **High** today was:

my **Low** today was:

my **Prayer** today is:

VERSE OF THE WEEK

The Lord bless you and keep you; the Lord make his face to shine upon you, and be gracious to you; the Lord lift up his countenance upon you, and give you peace.

Numbers 6:24-26

Learn sign language for this verse using FINKlink
BM13 @ www.faithink.com

ART ATTACK

Create your own artwork to help tell this week's story:

The Week in REVIEW

THIS WEEK'S BLESSING

(Name), child of God, may God bless you and keep you. May God's face shine upon you. May God be gracious to you and give you peace.

Looking back on the week, my highest **High** was:

....

My lowest **Low** this week was:

....

One way God answered my **Prayers** this week was:

....

One way God might use me as a **Sacred Agent** to help answer another person's prayers:

....

....

FAMILY COVENANT

Our family has shared **Highs & Lows** this week, **read** the cartoon Bible story and highlighted the theme verse in our Bibles, **talked** about our lives, **prayed** for one another's highs and lows, and **blessed** one another.

....

Parent's Signature   **Child's Signature**   **Date**

Name That Verse

1. **Divide** into small groups or teams.
2. **Listen** to eight short Bible Song clips at www.faithink.com.
3. **Guess** the location of each verse. Write your answer below.
4. **Award** the following points for each correct answer:

   * **Old or New Testament**   5 points
   * **Correct Bible Book, Chapter & Verse**   10 points

5. **Record** your scores immediately in the boxes to the right.
6. **Add** subtotal of all correct answers in the box. (80 Possible)
7. **Play** Bonus Round. Get all correct and score 20 extra pts.
8. **Total** results and award prizes for added fun.

Ark of the covenant by He Qi
www.HEQiARTS.com

Order this art print using FINKlink
BM13 @ www.faithink.com

Old or New Testament   Book, Chapter, Verse

Song 1

Song 2

Song 3

Song 4

Song 5

Song 6

Song 7

Song 8

Subtotal

Bonus Round
(Add 20 points if perfect order)

Play this online game using FINKlink
BM13 @ www.faithink.com

Final Score

Answer Key
Choose eight from the following verses

Genesis 1:1-3

Genesis 9:13-14

Genesis 15:5

Genesis 22:7-8

Genesis 28:11-13

Exodus 15:1

Exodus 20:2-3

Leviticus 19:2

Numbers 6:24-26

Numbers 23:19

Deuteronomy 6:6-9

Obadiah 1:15

FAITH INKUBATORS

Will He Not?

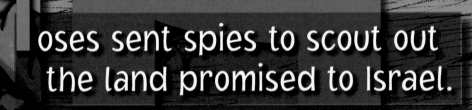

Moses sent spies to scout out the land promised to Israel.

After 40 days, the spies returned with their report. "The good news is, the land is rich! It overflows with milk and honey! The bad news is, these guys are huge! They will squash us like grasshoppers!"

HUGE!

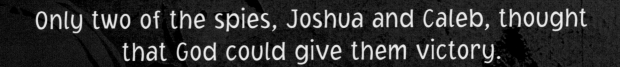

Only two of the spies, Joshua and Caleb, thought that God could give them victory.

We can take 'em!

If the Lord is pleased with us, he will give it to us.

Are you **crazy?** They are giants!

Why did you bring us here?

We're all gonna **die!**

Let's pick a new captain and go home!

Stone them!

Stone them!

The angry mob picked up rocks to kill them, but suddenly the glory of the Lord appeared. "I have had it! In spite of all that I have done for you, you still don't trust me," said God.

I will strike you down!

But Moses pleaded with God...

GSI (God Scene Investigation) Verse: Numbers 23:19, Leviticus 18:2

Find the hidden Bible verse in this cartoon and highlight it in your Bible. Then go to www.faithink.com and type in FINKlink BM14 to learn it in song and sign language.

VERSE OF THE WEEK

God is not a human being, that he should lie, or a mortal, that he should change his mind. Has he promised, and will he not do it? Has he spoken, and will he not fulfill it?

Speak to the people of Israel and say to them: I am the Lord your God.

Numbers 23:19 &
Leviticus 18:2

Day 1

my **High** today was:

my **Low** today was:

my **Prayer** today is:

Day 2

my **High** today was:

my **Low** today was:

my **Prayer** today is:

Day 3

my **High** today was:

my **Low** today was:

my **Prayer** today is:

Learn sign language for this verse using FINKlink

BM14 @ www.faithink.com

1. **Share** Highs & Lows of the day
2. **Read** sing, sign and highlight the verse of the week in your Bibles
3. **Talk** about how the verse relates to your Highs & Lows
4. **Pray** for your Highs & Lows, for your family and for the world
5. **Bless** one another using this week's blessing (bottom of next page)

Day 4

my **High** today was:

my **Low** today was:

my **Prayer** today is:

Day 5

my **High** today was:

my **Low** today was:

my **Prayer** today is:

Day 6

my **High** today was:

my **Low** today was:

my **Prayer** today is:

ART ATTACK

Create your own artwork to help tell this week's story:

The Week in REVIEW

THIS WEEK'S BLESSING

(Name), child of God, may you always trust in the promises of God.

Looking back on the week, my highest **High** was:

....

My lowest **Low** this week was:

....

One way God answered my **Prayers** this week was:

....

One way God might use me as a **Sacred Agent** to help answer another person's prayers:

....

....

FAMILY COVENANT

Our family has shared **Highs & Lows** this week, **read** the cartoon Bible story and highlighted the theme verse in our Bibles, **talked** about our lives, **prayed** for one another's highs and lows, and **blessed** one another.

....
Parent's Signature   **Child's Signature**   **Date**

Will He Not?

by Rich Melheim   **Online at www.faithink.com**
Numbers 23:19 & Leviticus 18:2

God is not a human being
that he should lie
or a mortal that he
should change his mind.
Has he promised,
will he not do it?
Has he spoken
and will he not fulfill it?

Will he not, will he not
will he not, will he not fulfill it?
Will he not, will he not
will he not, will he not fulfill it?

Speak to the people of Israel
(Israel, Israel)
Say to them "I am the Lord your God!"

Speak to the people of Israel
(Israel, Israel)
Say to them "I am
the Lord your God!"

Listen to this song using FINKlink
BM14 @ www.faithink.com

Day 1

my **High** today was:

my **Low** today was:

my **Prayer** today is:

Day 2

my **High** today was:

my **Low** today was:

my **Prayer** today is:

Day 3

my **High** today was:

my **Low** today was:

my **Prayer** today is:

1. **Share** Highs & Lows of the day
2. **Read** sing, sign and highlight the verse of the week in your Bibles
3. **Talk** about how the verse relates to your Highs & Lows
4. **Pray** for your Highs & Lows, for your family and for the world
5. **Bless** one another using this week's blessing (bottom of next page)

Day 4

my **High** today was:

my **Low** today was:

my **Prayer** today is:

Day 5

my **High** today was:

my **Low** today was:

my **Prayer** today is:

Day 6

my **High** today was:

my **Low** today was:

my **Prayer** today is:

VERSE OF THE WEEK

God is not a human being, that he should lie, or a mortal, that he should change his mind. Has he promised, and will he not do it? Has he spoken, and will he not fulfill it?

Speak to the people of Israel and say to them: I am the Lord your God.

Numbers 23:19 &
Leviticus 18:2

Art ATTACK

Create your own artwork to help tell this week's story:

The Week in Review

This Week's Blessing

(Name), child of God, may you always trust in the promises of God.

Looking back on the week, my highest **High** was:

My lowest **Low** this week was:

One way God answered my **Prayers** this week was:

One way God might use me as a **Sacred Agent** to help answer another person's prayers:

Family Covenant

Our family has shared **Highs & Lows** this week, **read** the cartoon Bible story and highlighted the theme verse in our Bibles, **talked** about our lives, **prayed** for one another's highs and lows, and **blessed** one another.

_____   _____   _____
Parent's Signature   Child's Signature   Date

Name That Verse

1. **Divide** into small groups or teams.
2. **Listen** to eight short Bible Song clips at www.faithink.com.
3. **Guess** the location of each verse. Write your answer below.
4. **Award** the following points for each correct answer:

   * **Old or New Testament**   5 points
   * **Correct Bible Book, Chapter & Verse** 10 points

5. **Record** your scores immediately in the boxes to the right.
6. **Add** subtotal of all correct answers in the box. (80 Possible)
7. **Play** Bonus Round. Get all correct and score 20 extra pts.
8. **Total** results and award prizes for added fun.

THE SPIES RETURN BY HE QI
www.HEQIARTS.com

Play this online game using FINKlink
BM14 @ www.faithink.com

Answer Key

CHOOSE EIGHT FROM THE FOLLOWING VERSES

Genesis 1:1-3

Genesis 3:8-9

Genesis 15:5

Genesis 22:7-8

Exodus 20:2-3

Leviticus 19:2

Numbers 6:24-26

Numbers 23:19

Deuteronomy 6:6-9

Proverbs 6:6-8

Matthew 691:1

John 4:13-14

	Old or New Testament	Book, Chapter, Verse	
Song 1			☐
Song 2			☐
Song 3			☐
Song 4			☐
Song 5			☐
Song 6			☐
Song 7			☐
Song 8			☐
		Subtotal	☐

Bonus Round
(Add 20 points if perfect order)   ☐ ☐ ☐ ☐ ☐

Play this online game using FINKlink
BM14 @ www.faithink.com

Final Score ☐

✚ FAITH INKUBATORS

Story no 15

Keep These Words

40

Listen to this song using FINKlink
BM15 @ www.faithink.com

Forty years passed from the time Moses sent spies into the land promised to Abraham and Sarah's children and the time God allowed Israel to enter. Every adult from the faithless generation was dead, except Joshua, Caleb and Moses. As they stood on the edge of the land, Moses made a request to God.

GSI (God Scene Investigation) Verse: Deuteronomy 6:4-9
Find the hidden Bible verse in this cartoon and highlight it in your Bible. Then go to
www.faithink.com and type in FINK*link* BM15 to learn it in song and sign language.

"Never speak of this matter again!" said God. "Go up to the top of the high hill. Take a look. But you will not cross it. Tell Joshua he will lead the people there!" And so God told Moses he would not be allowed to enter the land he had spent most of his life trying to find.

Moses obeyed and appointed General Joshua to lead Israel into the Promised Land. Then God gave Moses some final instructions:

"Tell Israel they are to be careful to keep all of my commandments. Don't let them slip from your minds.

Make them known to your children, and your children's children."

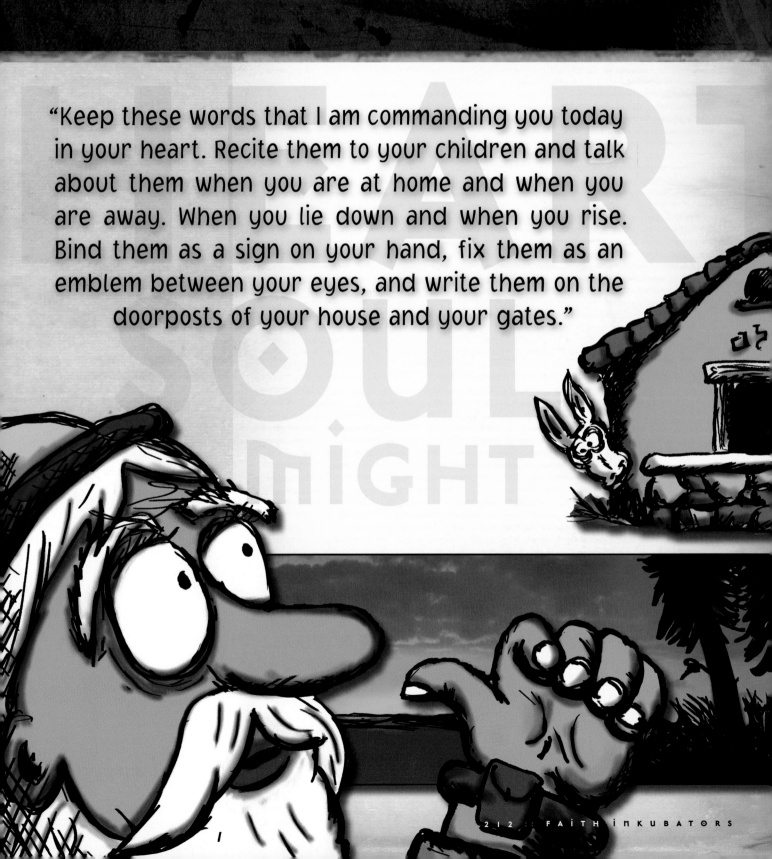

"Hear, O Israel: The Lord is our God, the Lord alone. You shall love the Lord your God will all your heart! And with all your soul! And with all your might!"

"Keep these words that I am commanding you today in your heart. Recite them to your children and talk about them when you are at home and when you are away. When you lie down and when you rise. Bind them as a sign on your hand, fix them as an emblem between your eyes, and write them on the doorposts of your house and your gates."

†hen Moses, the servant of the Lord, died and was buried in a valley in the land of Moab, but no one knows the burial place to this day.

The Home Huddle Journal
JOURNAL

Week 1

VERSE OF THE WEEK

Hear, O Israel: The Lord is our God, the Lord alone. You shall love the Lord your God with all your heart, and with all your soul, and with all your might. Keep these words that I am commanding you today in your heart. Recite them to your children and talk about them when you are at home and when you are away, when you lie down and when you rise. Bind them as a sign on your hand, fix them as an emblem on your forehead, and write them on the doorposts of your house and on your gates.

Deuteronomy 6:4-9

Learn sign language for this verse using FINKlink
BM15 | @ www.faithink.com

Day 1

my **High** today was:

my **Low** today was:

my **Prayer** today is:

Day 2

my **High** today was:

my **Low** today was:

my **Prayer** today is:

Day 3

my **High** today was:

my **Low** today was:

my **Prayer** today is:

1. **Share** Highs & Lows of the day
2. **Read** sing, sign and highlight the verse of the week in your Bibles
3. **Talk** about how the verse relates to your Highs & Lows
4. **Pray** for your Highs & Lows, for your family and for the world
5. **Bless** one another using this week's blessing (bottom of next page)

Day 4

my **High** today was:

my **Low** today was:

my **Prayer** today is:

Day 5

my **High** today was:

my **Low** today was:

my **Prayer** today is:

Day 6

my **High** today was:

my **Low** today was:

my **Prayer** today is:

Art
ATTACK

Create your own artwork to help tell this week's story:

R†he Week in EVIEW

†his Week's Blessing

(Name), child
of God, may you
always keep God's
Word in your
heart.

Looking back on the week, my highest **High** was:

....

My lowest **Low** this week was:

....

One way God answered my **Prayers** this week was:

....

One way God might use me as a **Sacred Agent** to help
answer another person's prayers:

....

....

Family Covenant

Our family has shared **Highs & Lows** this week, **read** the cartoon Bible story and high-
lighted the theme verse in our Bibles, **talked** about our lives, **prayed** for one another's
highs and lows, and **blessed** one another.

....

Parent's Signature   **Child's Signature**   **Date**

Keep These Words

by Rich Melheim   **Online at www.faithink.com**
Deuteronomy 6:4-9

Keep these words
that I am commanding you today
in your heart
Recite them to your children
and talk about them when
home and when away

When you lie down
and when you rise
bind them as a sign on your hand,
fix them as an emblem between your eyes

And write them on the doorposts
of your house,
write them on your gates
Keep these words
Keep these words

Hear, O Israel:
The Lord our God, the Lord alone
You shall love the Lord your God
with all your heart
I said with all your heart
with all your soul
with all your might
with all your might

Listen to this song using FINKlink
B M 1 5 @ www.faithink.com

JOURNAL

Week 2 (use this if you're doing a theme every 2 weeks)

Day 1

my **High** today was:

my **Low** today was:

my **Prayer** today is:

Day 2

my **High** today was:

my **Low** today was:

my **Prayer** today is:

Day 3

my **High** today was:

my **Low** today was:

my **Prayer** today is:

1. **Share** Highs & Lows of the day
2. **Read** sing, sign and highlight the verse of the week in your Bibles
3. **Talk** about how the verse relates to your Highs & Lows
4. **Pray** for your Highs & Lows, for your family and for the world
5. **Bless** one another using this week's blessing (bottom of next page)

Day 4

my **High** today was:

my **Low** today was:

my **Prayer** today is:

Day 5

my **High** today was:

my **Low** today was:

my **Prayer** today is:

Day 6

my **High** today was:

my **Low** today was:

my **Prayer** today is:

VERSE OF THE WEEK

Hear, O Israel: The Lord is our God, the Lord alone. You shall love the Lord your God with all your heart, and with all your soul, and with all your might. Keep these words that I am commanding you today in your heart. Recite them to your children and talk about them when you are at home and when you are away, when you lie down and when you rise. Bind them as a sign on your hand, fix them as an emblem on your forehead, and write them on the doorposts of your house and on your gates.

Deuteronomy 6:4-9

Learn sign language for this verse using FINKlink
BM15 @ www.faithink.com

ATTACK

Create your own artwork to help tell this week's story:

The Week in REVIEW

THIS WEEK'S BLESSING

(Name), child of God, may you always keep God's Word in your heart.

Looking back on the week, my highest **High** was:

....

My lowest **Low** this week was:

....

One way God answered my **Prayers** this week was:

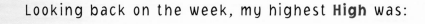

One way God might use me as a **Sacred Agent** to help answer another person's prayers:

....

....

FAMILY COVENANT

Our family has shared **Highs & Lows** this week, **read** the cartoon Bible story and highlighted the theme verse in our Bibles, **talked** about our lives, **prayed** for one another's highs and lows, and **blessed** one another.

....
Parent's Signature   **Child's Signature**   **Date**

Name That Verse

1. **Divide** into small groups or teams.
2. **Listen** to eight short Bible Song clips at www.faithink.com.
3. **Guess** the location of each verse. Write your answer below.
4. **Award** the following points for each correct answer:

   * **Old or New Testament**   5 points
   * **Correct Bible Book, Chapter & Verse**   10 points

5. **Record** your scores immediately in the boxes to the right.
6. **Add** subtotal of all correct answers in the box. (80 Possible)
7. **Play** Bonus Round. Get all correct and score 20 extra pts.
8. **Total** results and award prizes for added fun.

Moses Blesses Israel by He Qi
www.HEQIARTS.com

Order this art print using FINKlink
BM15 | @ www.faithink.com

Answer Key
Choose eight from the following verses

	Old or New Testament	Book, Chapter, Verse	
Song 1			☐
Song 2			☐
Song 3			☐
Song 4			☐
Song 5			☐
Song 6			☐
Song 7			☐
Song 8			☐
		Subtotal	☐

Genesis 1:1-3

Genesis 9:13-14

Genesis 15:5

Genesis 22:7-8

Genesis 28:11-13

Genesis 50:20

Leviticus 19:2

Numbers 6:24-26

Numbers 23:19

Deuteronomy 6:6-9

Joshua 1:9

Matthew 1:9

Bonus Round
(Add 20 points if perfect order)   ☐ ☐ ☐ ☐ ☐

Play this online game using FINKlink
BM15 | @ www.faithink.com

Final Score ☐

✛ FAITH
INKUBATORS

Looking back on the year, my highest **HIGH** was:

Take a moment to look back on the year and see how you, your family and your friends have changed and grown.

My lowest **LOW** this year was:

Paste **End of Year** photo of you here

(MY HOW YOU'VE GROWN)

This is Me

The Biggest way God answered my **PRAYER** this year:

Paste a photo of your **Family** here

This is My Family

One way I **GREW** in my faith this year was:

This is My Small Group

OPERATION SPYGLASS

Sacred agents get ready... It's time to get to know your
Bible Song living journal themes. Find each of the 75 items:

- ☐ Aaron (Moses' Brother)
- ☐ Abraham
- ☐ Adam
- ☐ Angels on a Ladder
- ☐ Ankle-Grabbing Jacob
- ☐ Apple (whole)
- ☐ Apple (Core)
- ☐ Ark of Noah
- ☐ Ark of the Covenant
- ☐ Baby Isaac (Laughter!)
- ☐ Birds Flying
- ☐ Burning Bush
- ☐ Camel
- ☐ Carrots
- ☐ Chariot
- ☐ Clam
- ☐ Commandment Tablets (smashed)
- ☐ Dog
- ☐ Dove
- ☐ Duck with Umbrella
- ☐ Ear Ring
- ☐ Elephant
- ☐ Esau
- ☐ Eve
- ☐ Faith Inkubators Logo
- ☐ Family
- ☐ Fish
- ☐ Frog
- ☐ Golden Calf
- ☐ Golden Goblet (Cup)
- ☐ Grapes
- ☐ Grasshopper
- ☐ Horse
- ☐ House
- ☐ Hummingbirds Feeding
- ☐ I Am
- ☐ Isaac (as a teenager)
- ☐ Jacob Sleeping

- ☐ Joseph's Multi-colored Coat
- ☐ Joshua
- ☐ Knife
- ☐ Manna
- ☐ Menorah (7 piece candlestick)
- ☐ Moon
- ☐ Moses (As a child writing)
- ☐ Mosquitoes
- ☐ Noah
- ☐ Old Jacob (Israel) Crying
- ☐ Parrot
- ☐ Passover Lamb (being sacrificed)
- ☐ Pharaoh
- ☐ Pharaoh's Daughter
- ☐ Phylactery (Ancient WWJD wrist band)
- ☐ Pillar of Fire (Leading Israel)
- ☐ Planet Earth
- ☐ Pyramid
- ☐ Quail
- ☐ Rainbow
- ☐ Ram Caught in a Thicket
- ☐ Rat
- ☐ Rebekah
- ☐ Red Sea Opening
- ☐ Sarah
- ☐ Shalom (Peace in Hebrew)
- ☐ Sheep
- ☐ Stars
- ☐ Snake
- ☐ Shield
- ☐ Spear
- ☐ Spies
- ☐ Tabernacle (Tent)
- ☐ Tambourine
- ☐ Thumbs Up & Down
- ☐ Two Turtles
- ☐ Yahweh

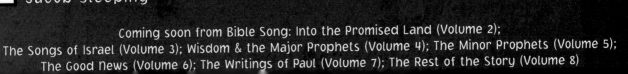

Coming soon from Bible Song: Into the Promised Land (Volume 2);
The Songs of Israel (Volume 3); Wisdom & the Major Prophets (Volume 4); The Minor Prophets (Volume 5);
The Good News (Volume 6); The Writings of Paul (Volume 7); The Rest of the Story (Volume 8)